Enrichment Masters

MATHEMATICS
Applications and Connections

Course 1

GLENCOE
McGraw-Hill

New York, New York
Columbus, Ohio
Mission Hills, California
Peoria, Illinois

Send all inquiries to:
Glencoe/McGraw-Hill
936 Eastwind Drive
Westerville, OH 43081

ISBN: 0-02-824617-9

4 5 6 7 8 9 10 11 12   024   02 01 00 99 98 97

CONTENTS

Glencoe Division, Macmillan/McGraw-Hill

Enrichment Worksheet 1-1

"What If...?" Questions

For many everyday problems, an important part of examining the solution is asking a "What if...?" question. Here is an example.

| 1. Explore |
| 2. Plan |
| 3. Solve |
| 4. Examine |

Tran wants to buy a bicycle that costs $192. He plans to save $6 each week. How many weeks will it take him to save enough money?

Solution: Divide $192 by $6. It will take 32 weeks.

What if...?   What if Tran could save $8 each week?

Result: Divide $192 by $8. It would take only 24 weeks.

Solve each problem. Then examine your solution and create a What if...? question. What is the result?

1. The distance from Chicago to Cleveland is 344 miles. Lisa plans to drive this distance in two days. If she drives 180 miles today, how many miles will she have to drive tomorrow?

   Solution:

   What if...?

   Result:

2. A one-year subscription to a popular magazine costs $24. Ted is thinking of sharing the cost of the subscription equally with two friends. How much will each have to pay?

   Solution:

   What if...?

   Result:

3. The Farrells want to buy a VCR that costs $460. They plan to make a down payment of $100 and pay the rest in eight equal payments. What will be the amount of each payment?

   Solution:

   What if...?

   Result:

4. Josita received $50 as a gift. She plans to buy two cassette tapes that cost $9 each and a deluxe headphone set that costs $25. How much money will she have left?

   Solution:

   What if...?

   Result:

Enrichment Worksheet 1-1

"What If...?" Questions

For many everyday problems, an important part of examining the solution is asking a "What if...?" question. Here is an example.

| 1. Explore |
| 2. Plan |
| 3. Solve |
| 4. Examine |

Tran wants to buy a bicycle that costs $192. He plans to save $6 each week. How many weeks will it take him to save enough money?

Solution: Divide $192 by $6. It will take 32 weeks.

What if...?   What if Tran could save $8 each week?

Result: Divide $192 by $8. It would take only 24 weeks.

Solve each problem. Then examine your solution and create a What if...? question. What is the result?

What if...? questions and results will vary. Samples are given.

1. The distance from Chicago to Cleveland is 344 miles. Lisa plans to drive this distance in two days. If she drives 180 miles today, how many miles will she have to drive tomorrow?

Solution: **164 miles**

What if...? **What if she drives 220 miles today?**

Result: **She only has to drive 124 miles tomorrow.**

2. A one-year subscription to a popular magazine costs $24. Ted is thinking of sharing the cost of the subscription equally with two friends. How much will each have to pay?

Solution: **$8**

What if...? **What if he shares the cost with only one friend?**

Result: **Each will pay $12.**

3. The Farrells want to buy a VCR that costs $460. They plan to make a down payment of $100 and pay the rest in eight equal payments. What will be the amount of each payment?

Solution: **$45**

What if...? **What if they make a down payment of $200?**

Result: **The amount of each payment will be only $32.50.**

4. Josita received $50 as a gift. She plans to buy two cassette tapes that cost $9 each and a deluxe headphone set that costs $25. How much money will she have left?

Solution: **$7**

What if...? **What if she buys just one cassette tape?**

Result: **She will have $16 left.**

Enrichment Worksheet 1-2

Newspaper Numbers

Many stories that you read in newspapers contain numbers. Sometimes these numbers are exact, and sometimes they are rounded. Do you know which is which?

In the headline at the right, the score of the game, 5-2, certainly is exact. However, the attendance probably was just a little more than 40,000 or a little less than 40,000. So 40,000 is most likely a rounded number.

The Benton Bugle
40,000 attend home opener
Tigers beat Twins, 5-2

Tell whether the number in each headline is more likely to be rounded or exact.

1. **Road construction to cost $3 million**

2. **Developer to build 65-story skyscraper**

3. **80 local families take part in national survey**

4. **Census: population increased by 8,500**

5. **One thousand homes without electricity**

6. **20 students honored at awards banquet**

7. **Maris hits 61st home run**

8. **Alvarez wins by 7,000 votes**

Circle the letter of the correct answer.

9. For a newspaper headline, the population of a country was rounded to 74 million. Which could be the actual population of this country?

   a. 73,098,500   **b.** 73,908,500   **c.** 74,598,500   **d.** 74,908,500

10. The actual amount of a city budget is $4,150,000. Which is the most appropriate way to round this amount for a headline?

    a. $4.1 million   **b.** $4.2 million   **c.** $4.5 million   **d.** $45 million

11. **CHALLENGE** The attendance at a concert was reported to be 6,000. If the number was rounded correctly to the nearest thousand, what is the least that the actual attendance could be? the greatest?

Glencoe Division, Macmillan/McGraw-Hill

Enrichment Worksheet 1-2

Newspaper Numbers

Many stories that you read in newspapers contain numbers. Sometimes these numbers are exact, and sometimes they are rounded. Do you know which is which?

In the headline at the right, the score of the game, 5-2, certainly is exact. However, the attendance probably was just a little more than 40,000 or a little less than 40,000. So 40,000 is most likely a rounded number.

The Benton Bugle
40,000 attend home opener
Tigers beat Twins, 5-2

Tell whether the number in each headline is more likely to be rounded or exact.

1. Road construction to cost $3 million **rounded**

2. Developer to build 65-story skyscraper **exact**

3. 80 local families take part in national survey **exact**

4. Census: population increased by 8,500 **rounded**

5. One thousand homes without electricity **rounded**

6. 20 students honored at awards banquet **exact**

7. Maris hits 61st home run **exact**

8. Alvarez wins by 7,000 votes **rounded**

Circle the letter of the correct answer.

9. For a newspaper headline, the population of a country was rounded to 74 million. Which could be the actual population of this country?

   a. 73,098,500   **b.** 73,908,500   c. 74,598,500   d. 74,908,500

10. The actual amount of a city budget is $4,150,000. Which is the most appropriate way to round this amount for a headline?

    a. $4.1 million   **b.** $4.2 million   c. $4.5 million   d. $45 million

11. **CHALLENGE** The attendance at a concert was reported to be 6,000. If the number was rounded correctly to the nearest thousand, what is the least that the actual attendance could be? the greatest?
    least: 5,500; greatest: 6,499

Glencoe Division, Macmillan/McGraw-Hill

Enrichment Worksheet 1-3

Using a Reference Point

There are many times when you need to make an estimate in relation to a **reference point.** For example, at the right there are prices listed for some school supplies. You might wonder if $5 is enough money to buy a small spiral notebook and a pen. This is how you might estimate, using $5 as the reference point.

- The notebook costs $1.59 and the pen costs $3.69.
- $1 + $3 = $4. I have $5 − $4, or $1, left.
- $0.59 and $0.69 are each more than $0.50, so $0.59 + $0.69 is more than $1.

So $5 will not be enough money.

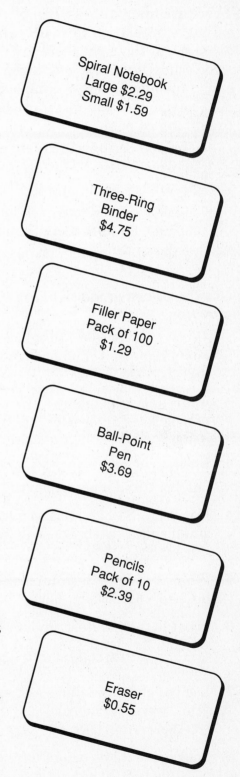

Spiral Notebook
Large $2.29
Small $1.59

Three-Ring Binder
$4.75

Filler Paper
Pack of 100
$1.29

Ball-Point Pen
$3.69

Pencils
Pack of 10
$2.39

Eraser
$0.55

Use the prices at the right to answer each question.

1. Jamaal has $5. Will that be enough money to buy a large spiral notebook and a pack of pencils?

2. Andreas wants to buy a three-ring binder and two packs of filler paper. Will $7 be enough money?

3. Rosita has $10. Can she buy a large spiral notebook and a pen and still have $5 left?

4. Kevin has $10 and has to buy a pen and two small spiral notebooks. Will he have $2.50 left to buy lunch?

5. What is the greatest number of erasers you can buy with $2?

6. What is the greatest amount of filler paper that you can buy with $5?

7. Lee bought three items and spent exactly $8.99. What were the items?

8. Select five items whose total cost is as close as possible to $10, but not more than $10.

Enrichment Worksheet 1-3

Using a Reference Point

There are many times when you need to make an estimate in relation to a **reference point.** For example, at the right there are prices listed for some school supplies. You might wonder if $5 is enough money to buy a small spiral notebook and a pen. This is how you might estimate, using $5 as the reference point.

- The notebook costs $1.59 and the pen costs $3.69.
- $1 + $3 = $4. I have $5 − $4, or $1, left.
- $0.59 and $0.69 are each more than $0.50, so $0.59 + $0.69 is more than $1.

So $5 will not be enough money.

Use the prices at the right to answer each question.

1. Jamaal has $5. Will that be enough money to buy a large spiral notebook and a pack of pencils? **yes**

2. Andreas wants to buy a three-ring binder and two packs of filler paper. Will $7 be enough money? **no**

3. Rosita has $10. Can she buy a large spiral notebook and a pen and still have $5 left? **no**

4. Kevin has $10 and has to buy a pen and two small spiral notebooks. Will he have $2.50 left to buy lunch? **yes**

5. What is the greatest number of erasers you can buy with $2? **3**

6. What is the greatest amount of filler paper that you can buy with $5?
3 packs, or 300 sheets

7. Lee bought three items and spent exactly $8.99. What were the items?
three-ring binder, pen, eraser

8. Select five items whose total cost is as close as possible to $10, but not more than $10.
Answers will vary. Sample: one pen, three packs of filler paper, one pack of pencils.

T3

Enrichment Worksheet 1-4

Finding a Range for a Product

Sometimes when you estimate a product you only need to find a **range** of reasonable numbers. For instance, here is how you can find a range for the product 28×153.

- Round each factor *down,* then multiply: $20 \times 100 = 2{,}000$.
- Round each factor *up,* then multiply: $30 \times 200 = 6{,}000$.

So the product 28×153 is between 2,000 and 6,000.

Find a range of reasonable numbers for each product.

1. 31×89 2. 65×384

3. 6×475 4. 80×146

Circle the letter of the best range for each product.

5. 67×95

    a. between 500 and 700
    b. between 5,000 and 7,000
    c. between 50,000 and 70,000

6. $47 \times 1{,}248$

    a. between 1,000 and 10,000
    b. between 10,000 and 100,000
    c. between 100,000 and 1,000,000

Using only the numbers in the box at the right, find two factors whose product is in each range. (Hint: A number may be multiplied by itself.)

7. less than 1,000   8. $1{,}000 \rightarrow 2{,}000$

9. $2{,}000 \rightarrow 3{,}000$ 10. $3{,}000 \rightarrow 4{,}000$

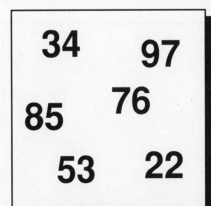

11. $4{,}000 \rightarrow 5{,}000$ 12. $5{,}000 \rightarrow 6{,}000$

13. $6{,}000 \rightarrow 7{,}000$ 14. $7{,}000 \rightarrow 8{,}000$

15. $8{,}000 \rightarrow 9{,}000$ 16. more than 9,000

Enrichment Worksheet 1-4

Finding a Range for a Product

Sometimes when you estimate a product you only need to find a **range** of reasonable numbers. For instance, here is how you can find a range for the product 28 × 153.

- Round each factor *down,* then multiply: 20 × 100 = 2,000.
- Round each factor *up,* then multiply: 30 × 200 = 6,000.

So the product 28 × 153 is between 2,000 and 6,000.

Find a range of reasonable numbers for each product.

1. 31 × 89
between 2,400 and 3,600

2. 65 × 384
between 18,000 and 28,000

3. 6 × 475
between 2,400 and 3,000

4. 80 × 146
between 8,000 and 16,000

Circle the letter of the best range for each product.

5. 67 × 95

   a. between 500 and 700
   b. between 5,000 and 7,000
   c. between 50,000 and 70,000

6. 47 × 1,248

   a. between 1,000 and 10,000
   b. between 10,000 and 100,000
   c. between 100,000 and 1,000,000

Using only the numbers in the box at the right, find two factors whose product is in each range. (Hint: A number may be multiplied by itself.)

Answers may vary.
Sample answers are given.

7. less than 1,000
22 and 34

8. 1,000 → 2,000
22 and 53

9. 2,000 → 3,000
34 and 76

10. 3,000 → 4,000
34 and 97

11. 4,000 → 5,000
53 and 76

12. 5,000 → 6,000
76 and 76

13. 6,000 → 7,000
76 and 85

14. 7,000 → 8,000
85 and 85

15. 8,000 → 9,000
85 and 97

16. more than 9,000
97 and 97

34   97
76
85
53   22

T4

Target Practice

In this activity, your target is an estimate and you take aim with a set of digits. It is your job to create a division problem whose answer is as close as possible to the target. For example, this is how you might aim at the target shown at the right.

$54 \div 9 = 6$, so $540 \div 9 = 60$.
537 is very close to 540, so
$537 \div 9$ would be very close to 60.

Answer: $\boxed{5}\ \boxed{3}\ \boxed{7} \div \boxed{9}$

digits: 3, 5, 7, 9

☐☐☐ ÷ ☐

Use the digits to create a division problem whose answer is as close as possible to the target. Each of the given digits should be used exactly once.

1.

digits: 2, 4, 6, 8

☐☐☐ ÷ ☐

2.

digits: 3, 4, 5, 6

☐☐☐ ÷ ☐

3.

digits: 1, 3, 4, 6

☐☐☐ ÷ ☐

4.

digits: 1, 3, 4, 6

☐☐☐ ÷ ☐

5.

digits: 0, 3, 5, 9

☐☐☐ ÷ ☐

6.

digits: 0, 2, 4, 5

☐☐☐ ÷ ☐

7. CHALLENGE Use the digits 0, 2, 4, 6, and 8 to create six different division problems whose answers are close to 500. In each division, each digit can be used exactly once.

Enrichment Worksheet 1-5

Target Practice

In this activity, your target is an estimate and you take aim with a set of digits. It is your job to create a division problem whose answer is as close as possible to the target. For example, this is how you might aim at the target shown at the right.

about 60

54 ÷ 9 = 6, so 540 ÷ 9 = 60.
537 is very close to 540, so
537 ÷ 9 would be very close to 60.

Answer: | 5 | 3 | 7 | ÷ | 9 |

digits: 3, 5, 7, 9

| | | | ÷ | |

Use the digits to create a division problem whose answer is as close as possible to the target. Each of the given digits should be used exactly once.

1.

about 40

digits: 2, 4, 6, 8

| 2 | 4 | 8 | ÷ | 6 |

2.

about 60

digits: 3, 4, 5, 6

| 3 | 5 | 4 | ÷ | 6 |

3.

about 80

digits: 1, 3, 4, 6

| 3 | 1 | 6 | ÷ | 4 |

4.

about 200

digits: 1, 3, 4, 6

| 6 | 1 | 4 | ÷ | 3 |

5.

about 200

digits: 0, 3, 5, 9

| 5 | 9 | 0 | ÷ | 3 |

6.

about 50

digits: 0, 2, 4, 5

| 2 | 0 | 5 | ÷ | 4 |

7. **CHALLENGE** Use the digits 0, 2, 4, 6, and 8 to create six different division problems whose answers are close to 500. In each division, each digit can be used exactly once.
2,068 ÷ 4; 2,086 ÷ 4; 4,026 ÷ 8; 4,062 ÷ 8; 2,840 ÷ 6; 2,804 ÷ 6

Enrichment Worksheet 1-6

Operations Puzzles

Now that you have learned how to evaluate an expression using the order of operations, can you work backwards? In this activity, the value of the expression will be given to you. It is your job to decide what the operations or the numbers must be in order to arrive at that value.

Fill in each ☐ **with +, −, ×, or ÷ to make a true statement.**

1. 48 ☐ 3 ☐ 12 = 12

2. 30 ☐ 15 ☐ 3 = 6

3. 24 ☐ 12 ☐ 6 ☐ 3 = 4

4. 24 ☐ 12 ☐ 6 ☐ 3 = 18

5. 4 ☐ 16 ☐ 2 ☐ 8 = 24

6. 45 ☐ 3 ☐ 3 ☐ 9 = 3

7. 36 ☐ 2 ☐ 3 ☐ 12 ☐ 2 = 0

8. 72 ☐ 12 ☐ 4 ☐ 8 ☐ 3 = 0

Fill in each ☐ **with one of the given numbers to make a true statement. Each number may be used only once.**

9. 6, 12, 24

☐ ÷ ☐ × ☐ = 12

10. 4, 9, 36

☐ − ☐ ÷ ☐ = 0

11. 6, 8, 12, 24

☐ ÷ ☐ + ☐ − ☐ = 4

12. 2, 5, 10, 50

☐ − ☐ ÷ ☐ + ☐ = 50

13. 2, 4, 6, 8, 10

☐ ÷ ☐ × ☐ + ☐ − ☐ = 0

14. 1, 3, 5, 7, 9

☐ ÷ ☐ + ☐ − ☐ ÷ ☐ = 1

15. CHALLENGE Fill in each ☐ with one of the digits from 1 through 9 to make a true statement. Each digit may be used only once.

☐ ÷ ☐ × ☐ + ☐ × ☐ × ☐ ÷ ☐ + ☐ × ☐ = 100

Enrichment Worksheet 1-6

Operations Puzzles

Now that you have learned how to evaluate an expression using the order of operations, can you work backwards? In this activity, the value of the expression will be given to you. It is your job to decide what the operations or the numbers must be in order to arrive at that value.

Fill in each ☐ with +, −, ×, or ÷ to make a true statement.

1. $48 \boxed{-} 3 \boxed{\times} 12 = 12$ 2. $30 \boxed{\div} 15 \boxed{\times} 3 = 6$

3. $24 \boxed{\div} 12 \boxed{+} 6 \boxed{\div} 3 = 4$ 4. $24 \boxed{-} 12 \boxed{\div} 6 \boxed{\times} 3 = 18$

5. $4 \boxed{\times} 16 \boxed{\div} 2 \boxed{-} 8 = 24$ 6. $45 \boxed{\div} 3 \boxed{-} 3 \boxed{-} 9 = 3$

7. $36 \boxed{\times} 2 \boxed{\div} 3 \boxed{-} 12 \boxed{\times} 2 = 0$ 8. $72 \boxed{-} 12 \boxed{\div} 4 \boxed{\times} 8 \boxed{\times} 3 = 0$

Fill in each ☐ with one of the given numbers to make a true statement. Each number may be used only once.

9. 6, 12, 24

$\boxed{24} \div \boxed{12} \times \boxed{6} = 12$

10. 4, 9, 36

$\boxed{4} - \boxed{36} \div \boxed{9} = 0$

11. 6, 8, 12, 24

$\boxed{24} \div \boxed{12} + \boxed{8} - \boxed{6} = 4$

12. 2, 5, 10, 50

$\boxed{2} - \boxed{10} \div \boxed{5} + \boxed{50} = 50$

13. 2, 4, 6, 8, 10

$\boxed{8} \div \boxed{4} \times \boxed{2} + \boxed{6} - \boxed{10} = 0$

14. 1, 3, 5, 7, 9

$\boxed{9} \div \boxed{3} + \boxed{5} - \boxed{7} \div \boxed{1} = 1$

Answers may vary. A sample answer is given.

15. **CHALLENGE** Fill in each ☐ with one of the digits from 1 through 9 to make a true statement. Each digit may be used only once.

$\boxed{9} \div \boxed{3} \times \boxed{8} + \boxed{7} \times \boxed{5} \times \boxed{4} \div \boxed{2} + \boxed{6} \times \boxed{1} = 100$

Enrichment Worksheet 1-7

What's in a Word?

Suppose that you use the following code for the letters of the alphabet.

A = 1	H = 8	O = 15	U = 21
B = 2	I = 9	P = 16	V = 22
C = 3	J = 10	Q = 17	W = 23
D = 4	K = 11	R = 18	X = 24
E = 5	L = 12	S = 19	Y = 25
F = 6	M = 13	T = 20	Z = 26
G = 7	N = 14		

$$\begin{array}{r} 13 \ (M) \\ \times \ \ 1 \ (A) \\ \hline 13 \\ \times \ 20 \ (T) \\ \hline 260 \\ \times \ \ 8 \ (H) \\ \hline 2{,}080 \end{array}$$

To evaluate a word using this code, you replace each letter with its code number, then multiply. For instance, at the right you see how to find the value of the word MATH, which is 2,080.

Use the code above to evaluate each word.

1. BOX

2. CUBE

3. TABLE

4. CATTLE

5. VARIABLE

6. ALGEBRA

Circle the word that has the greater value. (Hint: Do you have to evaluate the entire word, or is there a shortcut?)

7. PRINCIPAL or PRINCIPLE

8. MARCH or CHARM

9. THOUGHT or THROUGH

10. RIGHT or WRITE

Find a three-letter word that has a value as close as possible to the given number.

11. 1,000

12. 2,000

13. 3,000

14. 6,000

15. **CHALLENGE** What is the least possible value that you can find for a three-letter word? the greatest possible value?

What's in a Word?

Suppose that you use the following code for the letters of the alphabet.

A = 1	H = 8	O = 15	U = 21
B = 2	I = 9	P = 16	V = 22
C = 3	J = 10	Q = 17	W = 23
D = 4	K = 11	R = 18	X = 24
E = 5	L = 12	S = 19	Y = 25
F = 6	M = 13	T = 20	Z = 26
G = 7	N = 14		

$$
\begin{array}{r}
13 \;(M) \\
\times \quad 1 \;(A) \\
\hline
13 \\
\times \; 20 \;(T) \\
\hline
260 \\
\times \quad 8 \;(H) \\
\hline
2{,}080
\end{array}
$$

To evaluate a word using this code, you replace each letter with its code number, then multiply. For instance, at the right you see how to find the value of the word MATH, which is 2,080.

Use the code above to evaluate each word.

1. BOX **720**

2. CUBE **630**

3. TABLE **2,400**

4. CATTLE **72,000**

5. VARIABLE **427,680**

6. ALGEBRA **15,120**

Circle the word that has the greater value. (Hint: Do you have to evaluate the entire word, or is there a shortcut?)

7. PRINCIPAL or (PRINCIPLE)

8. MARCH or CHARM
Neither

9. (THOUGHT) or THROUGH

10. RIGHT or (WRITE)

Find a three-letter word that has a value as close as possible to the given number.
Answers may vary. Sample answers are given.

11. 1,000 **JET (value = 1,000)**

12. 2,000 **USE (value = 1,995)**

13. 3,000 **JOT (value = 3,000)**

14. 6,000 **TOT (value = 6,000)**

15. **CHALLENGE** What is the least possible value that you can find for a three-letter word? the greatest possible value?
Answers may vary. Samples: CAB (value = 6);
WOW (value = 7,935)

Enrichment Worksheet 1-8

Try This Balancing Act!

Do you think you can choose four of these numbers and place them on the balance scale at the right so that the two sums are equal?

32, 43, 44, 54, 55

Experiment. Put 32 and 43 on the left part of the scale. The sum is 75. Now try to pick two of the remaining numbers to make a sum of 75. Each pair of numbers you pick will total more than 75. You have to start over again. This time put 43 and 44 on the left part of the scale. The sum is 87. Put 32 and 55 on the right part of the scale. That sum is also 87. You succeeded on the second try!

$43 + 44 = 87$ $32 + 55 = 87$

Choose two numbers for the left part of the scale and two numbers for the right part so that the two sums are equal.

1. 12, 19, 36, 43

2. 42, 44, 63, 65

3. 12, 28, 51, 54, 67

4. 96, 101, 108, 112, 113

5. Balance the four parts of the scale at the right by choosing two of the numbers for each part of the scale.

4, 12, 13, 15, 17, 18, 19, 20, 21, 28

Try This Balancing Act!

Do you think you can choose four of these numbers and place them on the balance scale at the right so that the two sums are equal?

32, 43, 44, 54, 55

Experiment. Put 32 and 43 on the left part of the scale. The sum is 75. Now try to pick two of the remaining numbers to make a sum of 75. Each pair of numbers you pick will total more than 75. You have to start over again. This time put 43 and 44 on the left part of the scale. The sum is 87. Put 32 and 55 on the right part of the scale. That sum is also 87. You succeeded on the second try!

$$43 + 44 = 87 \qquad 32 + 55 = 87$$

Choose two numbers for the left part of the scale and two numbers for the right part so that the two sums are equal.

1. 12, 19, 36, 43

12, 43   **19, 36**

2. 42, 44, 63, 65

42, 65   **44, 63**

3. 12, 28, 51, 54, 67

12, 67   **28, 51**

4. 96, 101, 108, 112, 113

96, 113   **101, 108**

5. Balance the four parts of the scale at the right by choosing two of the numbers for each part of the scale.

4, 12, 13, 15, 17, 18, 19, 20, 21, 28

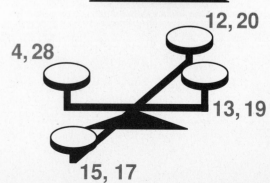

4, 28   **12, 20**

13, 19

15, 17

Enrichment Worksheet 1-9

Equation Chains

In an *equation chain,* you use the solution of one equation to help you find the solution of the next equation in the chain. The last equation in the chain is used to check that you have solved the entire chain correctly.

Complete each equation chain.

1. $5 + a = 12$,   so a = _____ .

    $ab = 14$,   so b = _____ .

    $16 \div b = c$,   so c = _____ .

    $14 - d = c$,   so d = _____ .

    $e \div d = 3$,   so e = _____ .

    $a + e = 25 \leftarrow$ **Check**

1. $9f = 36$,   so f = _____ .

    $g = 13 - f$,   so g = _____ .

    $63 \div g = h$,   so h = _____ .

    $h + i = 18$,   so i = _____ .

    $j - i = 9$,   so j = _____ .

    $j \div f = 5 \leftarrow$ **Check**

3. $m \div 4 = 8$,   so m = _____ .

    $m - n = 12$,   so n = _____ .

    $np = 100$,   so p = _____ .

    $q = 40 + p$,   so q = _____ .

    $p + q - 10 = r$, so r = _____ .

    $r - m = 8 \leftarrow$ **Check**

4. $18 = v - 12$, so v = _____ .

    $v \div w = 3$,   so w = _____ .

    $80 = wx$,   so x = _____ .

    $w + x = 2y$, so y = _____ .

    $xy - z = 40$, so z = _____ .

    $z - v = 2 \leftarrow$ **Check**

5. CHALLENGE Create your own equation chain using these numbers for the variables: $a = 10$, $b = 6$, $c = 18$, and $d = 3$.

Enrichment Worksheet 1-9

Equation Chains

In an *equation chain,* you use the solution of one equation to help you find the solution of the next equation in the chain. The last equation in the chain is used to check that you have solved the entire chain correctly.

Complete each equation chain.

1. $5 + a = 12$,   so $a = $ __7__ .

$ab = 14$,   so $b = $ __2__ .

$16 \div b = c$,   so $c = $ __8__ .

$14 - d = c$,   so $d = $ __6__ .

$e \div d = 3$,   so $e = $ __18__ .

$a + e = 25 \leftarrow$ **Check** $7 + 18 = 25$

1. $9f = 36$,   so $f = $ __4__ .

$g = 13 - f$,   so $g = $ __9__ .

$63 \div g = h$,   so $h = $ __7__ .

$h + i = 18$,   so $i = $ __11__ .

$j - i = 9$,   so $j = $ __20__ .

$j \div f = 5 \leftarrow$ **Check** $20 \div 4 = 5$

3. $m \div 4 = 8$,   so $m = $ __32__ .

$m - n = 12$,   so $n = $ __20__ .

$np = 100$,   so $p = $ __5__ .

$q = 40 + p$,   so $q = $ __45__ .

$p + q - 10 = r$, so $r = $ __40__ .

$r - m = 8 \leftarrow$ **Check** $40 - 32 = 8$

4. $18 = v - 12$, so $v = $ __30__ .

$v \div w = 3$,   so $w = $ __10__ .

$80 = wx$,   so $x = $ __8__ .

$w + x = 2y$, so $y = $ __9__ .

$xy - z = 40$, so $z = $ __32__ .

$z - v = 2 \leftarrow$ **Check** $32 - 30 = 2$

5. CHALLENGE Create your own equation chain using these numbers for the variables: $a = 10$, $b = 6$, $c = 18$, and $d = 3$.
Answers will vary. Sample: $12 - a = 2$;
$a = b + 4$; $3b = c$; $c \div d = 6$; $a - d = 7$

Enrichment Worksheet 1-10

Providing Needed Information

The problems on this page cannot be solved because they do not provide all the needed information. Your job is to make up reasonable information for what is missing. Then solve the problems. Here is an example.

Natalie earns $5 per hour as a cashier at Central Supermarket. How much did she earn last week?

Missing information: number of hours Natalie worked
New information: Natalie worked 12 hours last week.
Solution: Multiply $5 by 12. Natalie earned $60 last week.

1. Ramon worked 15 hours last week and earned $90. He deposited his entire paycheck into his savings account. What was the new balance in his account?

   Missing information:

   New information:

   Solution:

2. The cost of a wide-screen television is $840. Mary Ellen is going to share the cost equally with her brother and sisters. How much will each pay?

   Missing information:

   New information:

   Solution:

3. The Springfield Tigers won the last game of the season, beating the Midville Bears by a score of 6 to 5. To celebrate, Dave treated his two friends to lunch after the game. He left a $4 tip for the server. What was the total cost of the lunch and the tip?

   Missing information:

   New information:

   Solution:

4. The total attendance at the school play was 625 on Friday night, 430 on Saturday afternoon, and 750 on Saturday night. Tickets cost $4 for adults and $3 for students. What was the total amount collected from the sale of student tickets?

   Missing information:

   New information:

   Solution:

Enrichment Worksheet 1-10

Providing Needed Information

The problems on this page cannot be solved because they do not provide all the needed information. Your job is to make up reasonable information for what is missing. Then solve the problems. Here is an example.

Natalie earns $5 per hour as a cashier at Central Supermarket. How much did she earn last week?

Missing information:	number of hours Natalie worked
New information:	Natalie worked 12 hours last week.
Solution:	Multiply $5 by 12. Natalie earned $60 last week.

Answers will vary. Sample answers are given.

1. Ramon worked 15 hours last week and earned $90. He deposited his entire paycheck into his savings account. What was the new balance in his account?

   Missing information: **amount of money already in his account**

   New information: **Ramon had $640 in his savings account.**

   Solution: **$640 + $90 = $730**

2. The cost of a wide-screen television is $840. Mary Ellen is going to share the cost equally with her brother and sisters. How much will each pay?

   Missing information: **number of sisters**

   New information: **Mary Ellen has three sisters.**

   Solution: **$840 ÷ 5 = $168**

3. The Springfield Tigers won the last game of the season, beating the Midville Bears by a score of 6 to 5. To celebrate, Dave treated his two friends to lunch after the game. He left a $4 tip for the server. What was the total cost of the lunch and the tip?

   Missing information: **cost of the lunch**

   New information: **The cost of the lunch was $25.**

   Solution: **$25 + $4 = $29**

4. The total attendance at the school play was 625 on Friday night, 430 on Saturday afternoon, and 750 on Saturday night. Tickets cost $4 for adults and $3 for students. What was the total amount collected from the sale of student tickets?

   Missing information: **number of student tickets sold**

   New information: **There were 800 student tickets sold.**

   Solution: **800 × $3 = $2,400**

Enrichment Worksheet 2-1

The Binary Number System

Our standard number system in base ten has ten digits, 0 through 9. In base ten, the values of the places are powers of 10.

A system of numeration that is used in computer technology is the *binary number system*. In a **binary number**, the place value of each digit is two times the place value of the digit to its right. There are only two digits in the binary system: 0 and 1.

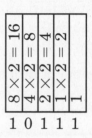

The binary number 10111 is written 10111_{two}. You can use a place-value chart like the one at the right to find the standard number that is equivalent to this number.

$$10111_{two} = 1 \times 16 + 0 \times 8 + 1 \times 4 + 1 \times 2 + 1 \times 1$$
$$= 16 + 0 + 4 + 2 + 1$$
$$= 23$$

Write each binary number as a standard number.

1. 11_{two} **2.** 111_{two} **3.** 100_{two}

4. 1001_{two} **5.** 11001_{two} **6.** 100101_{two}

Write each standard number as a binary number.

7. 8   **8.** 10   **9.** 15

10. 17   **11.** 28   **12.** 34

Write each answer as a binary number.

13. $1_{two} + 10_{two}$ **14.** $101_{two} - 10_{two}$

15. $10_{two} \times 11_{two}$ **16.** $10000_{two} \div 10_{two}$

17. CHALLENGE What standard number is equivalent to 12021_{three}?

Enrichment Worksheet 2-1

The Binary Number System

Our standard number system in base ten has ten digits, 0 through 9. In base ten, the values of the places are powers of 10.

A system of numeration that is used in computer technology is the *binary number system*. In a **binary number**, the place value of each digit is two times the place value of the digit to its right. There are only two digits in the binary system: 0 and 1.

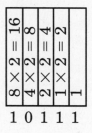

$$10\ 1\ 1\ 1$$

The binary number 10111 is written 10111_{two}. You can use a place-value chart like the one at the right to find the standard number that is equivalent to this number.

$$10111_{two} = 1 \times 16 + 0 \times 8 + 1 \times 4 + 1 \times 2 + 1 \times 1$$
$$= 16 + 0 + 4 + 2 + 1$$
$$= 23$$

Write each binary number as a standard number.

1. 11_{two} **3**

2. 111_{two} **7**

3. 100_{two} **4**

4. 1001_{two} **9**

5. 11001_{two} **25**

6. 100101_{two} **37**

Write each standard number as a binary number.

7. 8 1000_{two}

8. 10 1010_{two}

9. 15 1111_{two}

10. 17 10001_{two}

11. 28 11100_{two}

12. 34 100010_{two}

Write each answer as a binary number.

13. $1_{two} + 10_{two}$ 11_{two}

14. $101_{two} - 10_{two}$ 11_{two}

15. $10_{two} \times 11_{two}$ 110_{two}

16. $10000_{two} \div 10_{two}$ 1000_{two}

17. CHALLENGE   What standard number is equivalent to 12021_{three}?   **142**

Glencoe Division, Macmillan/McGraw-Hill

Enrichment Worksheet 2-2

Multiple Bar Graphs

Sometimes two related sets of data are displayed in a **double bar graph**. In this type of graph, two bars appear side-by-side in each category. A **legend** is included on the graph to help you distinguish between the bars.

For example, the graph at the right displays the average high and low temperatures for four cities. The legend appears in the upper-left corner.

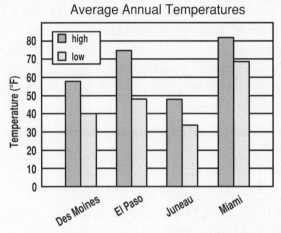

Average Annual Temperatures

Use the double bar graph at the right to answer each question.

1. Which city has the highest average low temperature?

2. About how many degrees greater is the average high temperature in El Paso than in Juneau?

3. The average high temperature in Juneau is about equal to the average low temperature in which city?

4. In which city is there the greatest difference between average high temperature and average low temperature?

Use the triple bar graph at the right to answer each question.

5. Write a brief paragraph describing the data that is displayed in the graph.

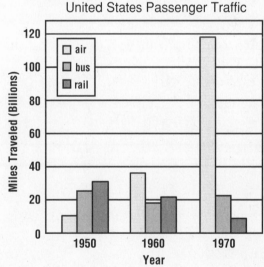

United States Passenger Traffic

6. What "message" do you think the graph is meant to convey?

Enrichment Worksheet 2-2

Multiple Bar Graphs

Sometimes two related sets of data are displayed in a **double bar graph**. In this type of graph, two bars appear side-by-side in each category. A **legend** is included on the graph to help you distinguish between the bars.

For example, the graph at the right displays the average high and low temperatures for four cities. The legend appears in the upper-left corner.

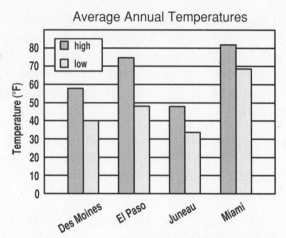

Average Annual Temperatures

Use the double bar graph at the right to answer each question.

1. Which city has the highest average low temperature?
Miami

2. About how many degrees greater is the average high temperature in El Paso than in Juneau? **about 30°F**

3. The average high temperature in Juneau is about equal to the average low temperature in which city?
El Paso

4. In which city is there the greatest difference between average high temperature and average low temperature?
El Paso

Use the triple bar graph at the right to answer each question.

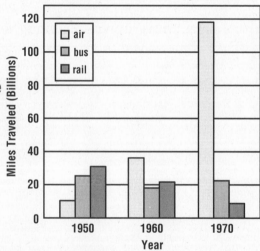

United States Passenger Traffic

5. Write a brief paragraph describing the data that is displayed in the graph.
Answers will vary. Sample: The graph shows data for the number of miles traveled by passengers in the United States in the years 1950, 1960, and 1970. Data are given for three types of transportation: air, bus, and rail.

6. What "message" do you think the graph is meant to convey?
Answers will vary. Sample: Between 1950 and 1970, people in the United States switched from doing most travel by rail to doing most travel by air. Because people could travel by air, the total number of miles they traveled increased greatly from 1960 to 1970.

Glencoe Division, Macmillan/McGraw-Hill

Enrichment Worksheet 2-3

Linguistic Statistics

Linguistics is the study of human speech. The activity on this page shows the type of data collection and analysis that might be done by a *linguist* who is researching the structure of the English language. All questions refer to the preamble to the U.S. Constitution, printed at the bottom of the page.

1. Which two consonants do you think appear most often in the preamble?

2. Which vowel do you think appears most often in the preamble? least often?

3. Complete this table by counting the occurrences of each letter. A few letters have been counted already, to help you get started. Hint: Your total should be 268.

Letter	Frequency	Letter	Frequency	Letter	Frequency
a		j		s	
b		k		t	
c		l		u	
d	11	m		v	
e		n	17	w	
f		o		x	
g		p		y	
h	9	q		z	
i		r	20		

4. Which two consonants actually appear most often in the preamble?

5. Which vowel actually appears most often in the preamble? least often?

6. Which *word* do you think occurs most often in the preamble? Verify your answer.

Preamble to the Constitution of the United States of America

We the People of the United States, in order to form a more perfect Union, establish justice, insure domestic tranquility, provide for the common defense, promote the general welfare, and secure the blessings of liberty to ourselves and our posterity, do ordain and establish this Constitution for the United States of America.

Enrichment Worksheet 2-3

Linguistic Statistics

Linguistics is the study of human speech. The activity on this page shows the type of data collection and analysis that might be done by a *linguist* who is researching the structure of the English language. All questions refer to the preamble to the U.S. Constitution, printed at the bottom of the page.

1. Which two consonants do you think appear most often in the preamble?
Answers will vary.

2. Which vowel do you think appears most often in the preamble? least often?
Answers will vary.

3. Complete this table by counting the occurrences of each letter. A few letters have been counted already, to help you get started. Hint: Your total should be 268.

Letter	Frequency	Letter	Frequency	Letter	Frequency
a	14	j	1	s	21
b	4	k	0	t	29
c	7	l	9	u	10
d	11	m	7	v	2
e	39	n	17	w	2
f	9	o	25	x	0
g	2	p	6	y	3
h	9	q	1	z	0
i	20	r	20		

4. Which two consonants actually appear most often in the preamble?
s and t

5. Which vowel actually appears most often in the preamble? least often?
e; u

6. Which *word* do you think occurs most often in the preamble? Verify your answer.
Answers may vary. ("the" occurs most frequently.)

Preamble to the Constitution of the United States of America

We the People of the United States, in order to form a more perfect Union, establish justice, insure domestic tranquility, provide for the common defense, promote the general welfare, and secure the blessings of liberty to ourselves and our posterity, do ordain and establish this Constitution for the United States of America.

Glencoe Division, Macmillan/McGraw-Hill

Enrichment Worksheet 2-4

Histograms

Often a graph is used to picture the data in a frequency table. When frequencies are pictured in a bar graph, the graph is called a **histogram**. For example, at the right is a histogram that pictures the frequencies of the scores on a math test. Each bar in a histogram shows the data in a certain interval.

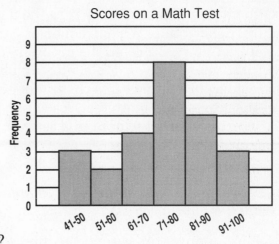

Scores on a Math Test

Use the histogram at the right to answer each question.

1. How many scores are in the interval 81–90?

2. In which interval(s) are there exactly three scores?

3. How many scores are 70 or less?

4. Suppose that, to pass this test, a student needed a score of 61 or higher. How many students passed the test?

5. Can you tell in which interval there is the greatest number of scores? Explain.

6. Can you tell what was the highest score on the test? Explain.

7. Use the histogram at the right. In the space below, write two questions about the data in the histogram. Then answer each question.

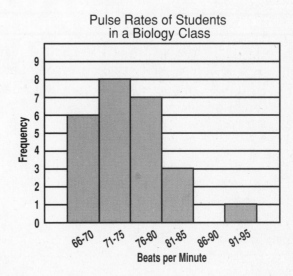

Pulse Rates of Students in a Biology Class

Enrichment Worksheet 2-4

Histograms

Often a graph is used to picture the data in a frequency table. When frequencies are pictured in a bar graph, the graph is called a **histogram**. For example, at the right is a histogram that pictures the frequencies of the scores on a math test. Each bar in a histogram shows the data in a certain interval.

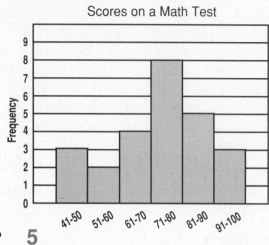

Scores on a Math Test

Use the histogram at the right to answer each question.

1. How many scores are in the interval 81–90?   **5**

2. In which interval(s) are there exactly three scores?
   41–50 and 91–100

3. How many scores are 70 or less?   **9**

4. Suppose that, to pass this test, a student needed a score of 61 or higher. How many students passed the test?   **20**

5. Can you tell in which interval there is the greatest number of scores? Explain.
   Yes; the bar for the interval 71–80 is the highest.

6. Can you tell what was the highest score on the test? Explain.
   No; you only know it was somewhere between 91–100.

7. Use the histogram at the right. In the space below, write two questions about the data in the histogram. Then answer each question.
   Answers will vary.

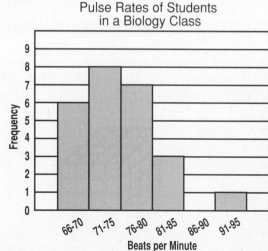

Pulse Rates of Students in a Biology Class

Beats per Minute

Enrichment Worksheet 2-5

Line Plots

In a **line plot**, data is pictured on a number line. An × is used
to represent each item of data. For example, the figure below is
a line plot that pictures data about the number of cassette tapes
owned by the students in a math class.

Number of Cassette Tapes Owned by Students in a Math Class

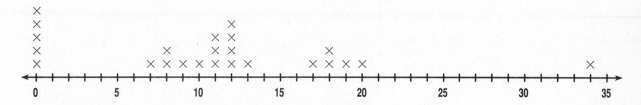

Use the line plot above to answer each question.

1. How many students own exactly eighteen tapes?

2. What number of tapes is owned by exactly three students?

3. A data item that is far apart from the rest of the data is
   called an **outlier**. Is there an outlier among these data?
   What is it?

4. What would you say is the number of tapes owned by the
   "typical" student in this class?

5. Use the data in this table to complete the line plot below.

Number of Seconds for 24 Sixth-Graders to Run 200 Meters											
130	100	85	120	100	100	110	150	90	100	110	130
125	105	100	70	125	85	95	130	105	90	105	100

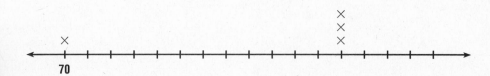

Glencoe Division, Macmillan/McGraw-Hill

Enrichment Worksheet 2-5

Line Plots

In a **line plot**, data is pictured on a number line. An × is used
to represent each item of data. For example, the figure below is
a line plot that pictures data about the number of cassette tapes
owned by the students in a math class.

Number of Cassette Tapes Owned by Students in a Math Class

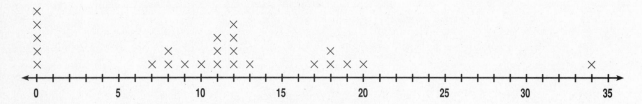

Use the line plot above to answer each question.

1. How many students own exactly eighteen tapes? **2**

2. What number of tapes is owned by exactly three students?
11

3. A data item that is far apart from the rest of the data is
called an **outlier**. Is there an outlier among these data?
What is it? **Yes; 34**

4. What would you say is the number of tapes owned by the
"typical" student in this class?
Answers may vary. Possible response: 7–13

5. Use the data in this table to complete the line plot below.

Number of Seconds for 24 Sixth-Graders to Run 200 Meters											
130	100	85	120	100	100	110	150	90	100	110	130
125	105	100	70	125	85	95	130	105	90	105	100

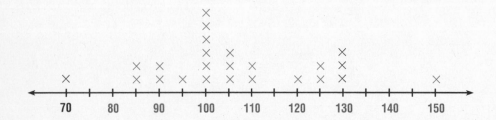

Enrichment Worksheet 2-6

Graphs and Decision Making

Just as important as knowing how to make a bar graph or a line graph is deciding what type of graph to use. Here are some guidelines to help you make that decision.

- A bar graph compares data that fall into distinct categories.

- A line graph shows changes in data over a period of time.

Example Use a bar graph to show how the populations of several cities compare in one year.

Example Use a line graph to show how the population of one city changed over several years.

Would you use a bar graph or a line graph to show these data?

1. average temperatures in Sacramento for each month of the year

2. average temperatures in January in five California cities

3. land area of the continents

4. number of CD players used each year from 1981 through 1990

5. weight of a baby in each month from birth to one year of age

6. heights of the world's five tallest buildings

Make an appropriate graph for each set of data.

7. **Cars in Use**

Year	Number (Millions)
1970	80
1980	105
1990	124

8. **Seating Capacity of Aircraft**

Model	Number of Seats
B747	405
DC-10	288
L-1011	296
MD-80	142

Enrichment Worksheet 2-6

Graphs and Decision Making

Just as important as knowing how to make a bar graph or a line graph is deciding what type of graph to use. Here are some guidelines to help you make that decision.

• A bar graph compares data that fall into distinct categories.

• A line graph shows changes in data over a period of time.

Example Use a bar graph to show how the populations of several cities compare in one year.

Example Use a line graph to show how the population of one city changed over several years.

Would you use a bar graph or a line graph to show these data?

1. average temperatures in Sacramento for each month of the year   **line graph**

2. average temperatures in January in five California cities   **bar graph**

3. land area of the continents   **bar graph**

4. number of CD players used each year from 1981 through 1990   **line graph**

5. weight of a baby in each month from birth to one year of age   **line graph**

6. heights of the world's five tallest buildings   **bar graph**

Make an appropriate graph for each set of data.

7.   **Cars in Use**

Year	Number (Millions)
1970	80
1980	105
1990	124

8.   **Seating Capacity of Aircraft**

Model	Number of Seats
B747	405
DC-10	288
L-1011	296
MD-80	142

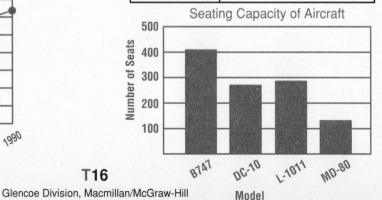

Glencoe Division, Macmillan/McGraw-Hill

Enrichment Worksheet 2-7

Puzzling over Data

Each puzzle on this page contains an incomplete set of data. The clues give you information about the mean, median, mode, or range of the data. Working from these clues, you can decide what the missing data items must be. For example, this is how you might solve the data puzzle at the right.

Clue: mean = 18

Data: 12, 17, 18, 19, 19, ☐

There are 6 items of data.
The mean is 18, so the sum of the data must be $6 \times 18 = 108$.
Add the given data: $12 + 17 + 18 + 19 + 19 = 85$
Subtract from 108: $108 - 85 = 23$

So the complete set of data is: 12, 17, 18, 19, 19, $\boxed{23}$

Find the missing data. (Assume that the data items are listed in order from least to greatest.)

1. *Clue:* mode = 8

   Data: 7, 7, 8, ☐, ☐, 14

2. *Clue:* median = 54.5

   Data: 36, 40, 49, ☐, 65, 84

3. *Clues:* mean = 27
           mode = 30

   Data: 10, 25, 27, ☐, 30, ☐

4. *Clues:* median = 120
           range = 46

   Data: 110, 112, ☐, 124, 136, ☐

5. *Clues:* mean = 13
           median = 13
           range = 13

   Data: ☐, 9, 12, ☐, 18, ☐

6. *Clues:* mean = 7
           median = 8.5
           mode = 10

   Data: ☐, 4, 8, ☐, ☐, ☐

7. *Clues:* mean = 60
           mode = 52
           range = 28

   Data: ☐, 52, ☐, ☐, 72, 78

8. *Clues:* median = 24
           mode = 28
           range = 24

   Data: 6, 15, ☐, ☐, ☐, ☐

Enrichment Worksheet 2-7

Puzzling over Data

Each puzzle on this page contains an incomplete set of data. The clues give you information about the mean, median, mode, or range of the data. Working from these clues, you can decide what the missing data items must be. For example, this is how you might solve the data puzzle at the right.

Clue: mean = 18

Data: 12, 17, 18, 19, 19, ☐

There are 6 items of data.
The mean is 18, so the sum of the data must be 6 × 18 = 108.
Add the given data: 12 + 17 + 18 + 19 + 19 = 85
Subtract from 108: 108 − 85 = 23

So the complete set of data is: 12, 17, 18, 19, 19, 23

Find the missing data. (Assume that the data items are listed in order from least to greatest.)

1. *Clue:* mode = 8

Data: 7, 7, 8, 8 , 8 , 14

2. *Clue:* median = 54.5

Data: 36, 40, 49, 60 , 65, 84

3. *Clues:* mean = 27
mode = 30

Data: 10, 25, 27, 30 , 30, 40

4. *Clues:* median = 120
range = 46

Data: 110, 112, 116 , 124, 136, 156

5. *Clues:* mean = 13
median = 13
range = 13

Data: 6 , 9, 12, 14 , 18, 19

6. *Clues:* mean = 7
median = 8.5
mode = 10

Data: 1 , 4, 8, 9 , 10 , 10

7. *Clues:* mean = 60
mode = 52
range = 28

Data: 50 , 52, 52 , 56 , 72, 78

8. *Clues:* median = 24
mode = 28
range = 24

Data: 6, 15, 20 , 28 , 28 , 30

Enrichment Worksheet 2-8

Be a Data Detective!

Each of the graphs on this page has been drawn incorrectly.
Can you detect the mistake?

1. Weekly Book Sales

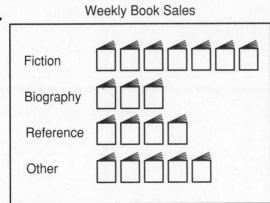

Mistake:

2. United States Population

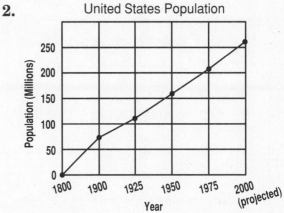

Mistake:

3. Areas of the Great Lakes

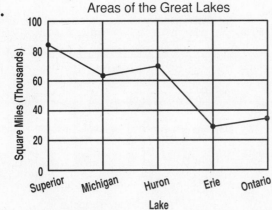

Mistake:

4. Retail Sales of Automobiles

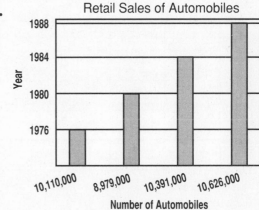

Mistake:

5. Draw a corrected graph for Exercise 3.

6. Draw a corrected graph for Exercise 4.

Enrichment Worksheet 2-8

Be a Data Detective!

Each of the graphs on this page has been drawn incorrectly.
Can you detect the mistake?

1. Weekly Book Sales

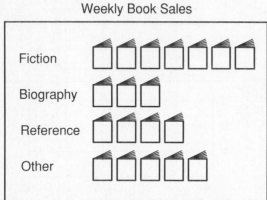

Mistake: **Missing information about what each symbol means.**

2. United States Population

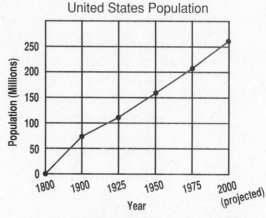

Mistake: **Interval from 1800–1900 is not equal to other intervals.**

3. Areas of the Great Lakes

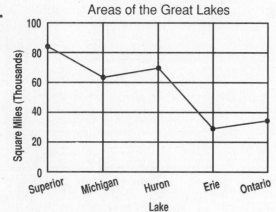

Mistake: **Line graph is not appropriate for these data.**

4. Retail Sales of Automobiles

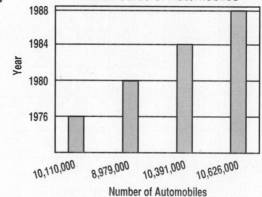

Mistake: **Axes are reversed.**

5. Draw a corrected graph for Exercise 3.

Areas of the Great Lakes

6. Draw a corrected graph for Exercise 4.

Retail Sales of Automobiles

T18

Enrichment Worksheet 3-1

Decimal Letters

The letter **A** at the right was created by shading part of a hundredssquare. There are 26 parts shaded, so the *value* of the letter **A** is 26 hundredths, or 0.26.

Find the value of each letter.

1. 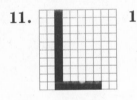   2. 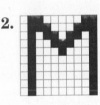   3. 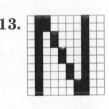   4. 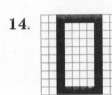   5.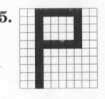

6. 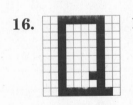   7. 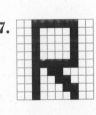   8. 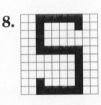   9. 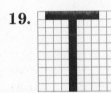   10.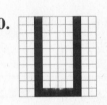

11. 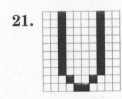   12. 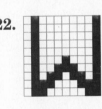   13. 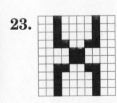   14. 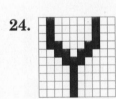   15.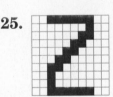

16.   17.   18.   19.   20.

21.   22.   23.   24.   25.

26. **CHALLENGE**   Use the values of the 26 letters as a set of data. What is the frequency of the value 0.26? Which value is the mode?

Glencoe Division, Macmillan/McGraw-Hill

Enrichment Worksheet 3-1

Decimal Letters

The letter **A** at the right was created by shading part of a hundredssquare. There are 26 parts shaded, so the *value* of the letter **A** is 26 hundredths, or 0.26.

Find the value of each letter.

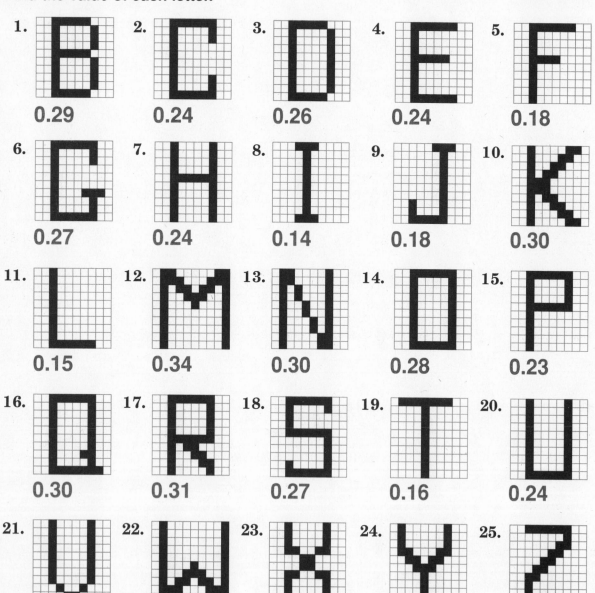

1. 0.29
2. 0.24
3. 0.26
4. 0.24
5. 0.18

6. 0.27
7. 0.24
8. 0.14
9. 0.18
10. 0.30

11. 0.15
12. 0.34
13. 0.30
14. 0.28
15. 0.23

16. 0.30
17. 0.31
18. 0.27
19. 0.16
20. 0.24

21. 0.20
22. 0.34
23. 0.24
24. 0.21
25. 0.25

26. **CHALLENGE** Use the values of the 26 letters as a set of data. What is the frequency of the value 0.26? Which value is the mode? **2; 0.24**

Enrichment Worksheet 3-2

Writing Checks

When you write a personal check, the amount is written once in decimal form and a second time in word form.

```
                                                    1043
Melissa Chin                                        6-10
29411 Oak Avenue                                    ----
Springfield, Tennessee 37172    May 14   19 92      140

Pay to the
order of ___Stimson's_____   $ 43.95_____

   Forty-three and 95/100 _____ Dollars

Town Savings Bank
for  books_____        Melissa Chin_____

000147721 0039244910 1043
```

Notice that in the word form the cents are written as a fractional part of a dollar. A whole-number amount, like $25.00, would be written as *Twenty-five and 00/100.*

Write each amount in decimal form.

1. Seven and 46/100 dollars

2. Eighty-two and 00/100 dollars

3. Thirty and 5/100 dollars

4. Two hundred and 9/100 dollars

Write each amount in words as it would appear on a check.

5. $15.75

6. $312.49

7. $1,000

8. $46.02

Use the check at the top of the page to answer each question.

9. What is the date of the check? the name of the bank?

10. Do you think the check would be valid if Melissa did not sign it?

11. Would the check be valid if Melissa did not indicate its purpose?

12. Why do you think the amount is written in two ways?

Enrichment Worksheet 3-2

Writing Checks

When you write a personal check, the amount is written once in decimal form and a second time in word form.

```
Melissa Chin                                              1043
29411 Oak Avenue                                          6-10
Springfield, Tennessee 37172        May 14    19 92       140

Pay to the
order of    Stimson's                        $ 43.95

  Forty-three and 95/100                              Dollars

Town Savings Bank
for  books                    Melissa Chin

000147721 0039244910 1043
```

Notice that in the word form the cents are written as a fractional part of a dollar. A whole-number amount, like $25.00, would be written as *Twenty-five and 00/100*.

Write each amount in decimal form.

1. Seven and 46/100 dollars
   $7.46

2. Eighty-two and 00/100 dollars
   $82.00

3. Thirty and 5/100 dollars
   $30.05

4. Two hundred and 9/100 dollars
   $200.09

Write each amount in words as it would appear on a check.

5. $15.75
   Fifteen and 75/100 dollars

6. $312.49
   Three hundred twelve and 49/100 dollars

7. $1,000
   One thousand and 00/100 dollars

8. $46.02
   Forty-six and 2/100 dollars

Use the check at the top of the page to answer each question.

9. What is the date of the check? the name of the bank?
   May 14, 1992; Town Savings Bank

10. Do you think the check would be valid if Melissa did not sign it? **no**

11. Would the check be valid if Melissa did not indicate its purpose? **yes**

12. Why do you think the amount is written in two ways?
    To avoid writing the wrong amount.

Enrichment Worksheet 3-3

A Metric Crossword Puzzle

Here is a crossword puzzle with a "twist." To locate the first letter of each word, you have to measure from the upper left corner of the puzzle. Each square of the puzzle measures 1 cm on each side. The first word has been entered for you, to help you get started. Good luck!

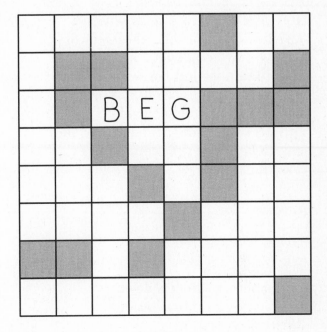

Across

2.5 cm across, 25 mm down
Ask

6.5 cm across, 35 mm down
Compact disc (abbreviation)

0.5 cm across, 55 mm down
Thin, pointed piece of metal

3.5 cm across, 15 mm down
Light red

4.5 cm across, 65 mm down
Customary unit of length

6.5 cm across, 5 mm down
Opposite of P.M.

5.5 cm across, 55 mm down
Boy's name

3.5 cm across, 35 mm down
New Hampshire (abbreviation)

0.5 cm across, 5 mm down
Yellow, egg-shaped fruit

6.5 cm across, 45 mm down
Greeting

0.5 cm across, 35 mm down
Face-_?_-face

0.5 cm across, 45 mm down
Type of tree

0.5 cm across, 75 mm down
Saturday and Sunday

Down

65 mm across, 3.5 cm down
Young person

35 mm across, 0.5 cm down
Opposite of closed

75 mm across, 3.5 cm down
Ten cents

15 mm across, 3.5 cm down
Wave in Spanish

65 mm across, 0.5 cm down
Alaska (abbreviation)

25 mm across, 4.5 cm down
Belonging to me

45 mm across, 0.5 cm down
Opposite of day

55 mm across, 5.5 cm down
Type of metal

5 mm across, 0.5 cm down
Pay attention

45 mm across, 6.5 cm down
Maine (abbreviation)

Enrichment Worksheet 3-3

A Metric Crossword Puzzle

Here is a crossword puzzle with a "twist." To locate the first letter of each word, you have to measure from the upper left corner of the puzzle. Each square of the puzzle measures 1 cm on each side. The first word has been entered for you, to help you get started. Good luck!

Crossword grid:

L	E	M	O	N		A	M
I			P	I	N	K	
S		B	E	G			
T	O		N	H		C	D
E	L	M		T		H	I
N	A	I	L		T	I	M
			N		M	I	L	E
W	E	E	K	E	N	D	

Across

2.5 cm across, 25 mm down
Ask

6.5 cm across, 35 mm down
Compact disc (abbreviation)

0.5 cm across, 55 mm down
Thin, pointed piece of metal

3.5 cm across, 15 mm down
Light red

4.5 cm across, 65 mm down
Customary unit of length

6.5 cm across, 5 mm down
Opposite of P.M.

5.5 cm across, 55 mm down
Boy's name

3.5 cm across, 35 mm down
New Hampshire (abbreviation)

0.5 cm across, 5 mm down
Yellow, egg-shaped fruit

6.5 cm across, 45 mm down
Greeting

0.5 cm across, 35 mm down
Face-_?_-face

0.5 cm across, 45 mm down
Type of tree

0.5 cm across, 75 mm down
Saturday and Sunday

Down

65 mm across, 3.5 cm down
Young person

35 mm across, 0.5 cm down
Opposite of closed

75 mm across, 3.5 cm down
Ten cents

15 mm across, 3.5 cm down
Wave in Spanish

65 mm across, 0.5 cm down
Alaska (abbreviation)

25 mm across, 4.5 cm down
Belonging to me

45 mm across, 0.5 cm down
Opposite of day

55 mm across, 5.5 cm down
Type of metal

5 mm across, 0.5 cm down
Pay attention

45 mm across, 6.5 cm down
Maine (abbreviation)

Enrichment Worksheet 3-4

A Look at Nutrients

The table below gives data about a few of the nutrients in an average serving of some common foods.

Food	Protein (grams)	Fat (grams)	Carbohydrates (grams)	Vitamins (milligrams)			Minerals* (milligrams)		
				B	B-1	B-2	Na	K	Ca
apple (medium)	0.3	0.5	21.1	8	0.02	0.02	1	159	10
chocolate bar (1.02 oz)	2.2	9.4	16.5	0	0.02	0.08	26	119	55
cola (12 fl oz)	0.0	0.0	40.7	0	0.00	0.00	20	7	11
hamburger (1 medium)	21.8	14.5	0.0	0	0.13	0.15	40	382	6
orange juice (8 fl oz)	1.7	0.1	26.8	97	0.20	0.05	2	474	22
peas (1/2 cup)	4.5	0.4	10.8	19	0.22	0.09	128	137	17
wheat bread (1 slice)	2.3	1.0	11.3	0	0.11	0.08	129	33	30
whole milk (8 fl oz)	8.0	8.2	11.4	2	0.09	0.40	120	370	291

*Na = sodium K = potassium Ca = calcium

Use the data in the table to answer each question.

1. Is there more potassium in one apple or in one serving of peas?

2. Does one serving of milk contain more fat or more carbohydrates?

3. Which foods contain less than 0.05 milligram of vitamin B-2?

4. Which foods contain an amount of carbohydrates between 15 grams and 25 grams?

5. Which food contains the least amount of calcium?

6. Which food contains the greatest amount of vitamin B-1?

7. List the foods in order of their protein content from least to greatest.

8. List the foods in order of their fat content from greatest to least.

9. Make up two questions about the data in the table. Exchange questions with a classmate. Then answer your classmate's questions.

Enrichment Worksheet 3-4

A Look at Nutrients

The table below gives data about a few of the nutrients in an average serving of some common foods.

Food	Protein (grams)	Fat (grams)	Carbohydrates (grams)	Vitamins (milligrams)			Minerals* (milligrams)		
				B	B-1	B-2	Na	K	Ca
apple (medium)	0.3	0.5	21.1	8	0.02	0.02	1	159	10
chocolate bar (1.02 oz)	2.2	9.4	16.5	0	0.02	0.08	26	119	55
cola (12 fl oz)	0.0	0.0	40.7	0	0.00	0.00	20	7	11
hamburger (1 medium)	21.8	14.5	0.0	0	0.13	0.15	40	382	6
orange juice (8 fl oz)	1.7	0.1	26.8	97	0.20	0.05	2	474	22
peas (1/2 cup)	4.5	0.4	10.8	19	0.22	0.09	128	137	17
wheat bread (1 slice)	2.3	1.0	11.3	0	0.11	0.08	129	33	30
whole milk (8 fl oz)	8.0	8.2	11.4	2	0.09	0.40	120	370	291

*Na = sodium K = potassium Ca = calcium

Use the data in the table to answer each question.

1. Is there more potassium in one apple or in one serving of peas?   **apple**

2. Does one serving of milk contain more fat or more carbohydrates?
   carbohydrates

3. Which foods contain less than 0.05 milligram of vitamin B-2?   **apple, cola**

4. Which foods contain an amount of carbohydrates between 15 grams and 25 grams?   **apple, chocolate bar**

5. Which food contains the least amount of calcium?   **hamburger**

6. Which food contains the greatest amount of vitamin B-1?   **peas**

7. List the foods in order of their protein content from least to greatest.   **cola, apple, orange juice, chocolate bar, wheat bread, peas, whole milk, hamburger**

8. List the foods in order of their fat content from greatest to least.
   hamburger, chocolate bar, whole milk, wheat bread, apple, peas, orange juice, cola

9. Make up two questions about the data in the table. Exchange questions with a classmate. Then answer your classmate's questions.
   Answers will vary.

Enrichment Worksheet 3-5

Everybody into the Pool!

Answer each question using the "decimal pool" below.

1. Which decimal when rounded to the nearest hundredth is 0.03?

2. Which decimal when rounded to the nearest thousandth is 0.003?

3. Which two decimals when rounded to the nearest hundredth are 0.02?

4. Which five decimals when rounded to the nearest tenth are 0.2?

5. Which decimal when rounded to the nearest thousandth is 0.210?

6. Which two decimals when rounded to the nearest hundredth are 0.20?

7. Add to the pool four different decimals that when rounded to the nearest thousandth are 0.301.

8. Add to the pool a three-place decimal that when rounded to the nearest tenth is 1.0.

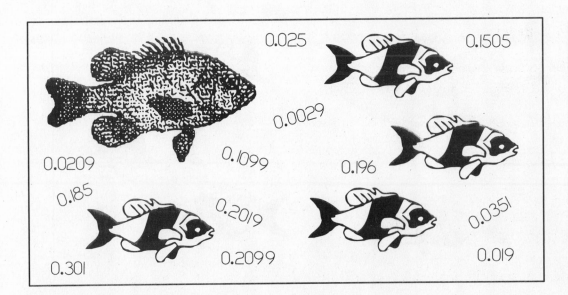

0.025   0.1505   0.0029   0.0209   0.1099   0.196   0.185   0.2019   0.301   0.2099   0.0351   0.019

9. *CHALLENGE*   Suppose that you are rounding decimals to the nearest hundredth. How many three-place decimals round to 0.05? List them. How many four-place decimals do you think round to 0.05?

Enrichment Worksheet 3-5

Everybody into the Pool!

Answer each question using the "decimal pool" below.

1. Which decimal when rounded to the nearest hundredth is 0.03?
0.025

2. Which decimal when rounded to the nearest thousandth is 0.003?
0.0029

3. Which two decimals when rounded to the nearest hundredth are 0.02?
0.0209, 0.019

4. Which five decimals when rounded to the nearest tenth are 0.2? **0.185, 0.196, 0.1505, 0.2019, 0.2099**

5. Which decimal when rounded to the nearest thousandth is 0.210?
0.2099

6. Which two decimals when rounded to the nearest hundredth are 0.20?
0.196, 0.2019

7. Add to the pool four different decimals that when rounded to the nearest thousandth are 0.301.
Answers will vary.

8. Add to the pool a three-place decimal that when rounded to the nearest tenth is 1.0.
Answers will vary.

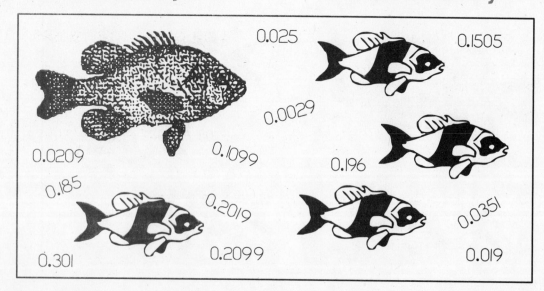

9. **CHALLENGE** Suppose that you are rounding decimals to the nearest hundredth. How many three-place decimals round to 0.05? List them. How many four-place decimals do you think round to 0.05?
ten; 0.045, 0.046, 0.047, 0.048, 0.049, 0.050, 0.051, 0.052, 0.053, 0.054; one hundred

Glencoe Division, Macmillan/McGraw-Hill

Enrichment Worksheet 3-6

Horizontal Front-End Estimation

Many times an addition problem is given to you in *horizontal form*, with the addends written from left to right. To estimate the sum, you don't have to rewrite the addition vertically in order to line up the decimal points. Just use place value to figure out which digits are most important. Here is an example.

3.11 + 0.4639 + 8.205

The most important digits are in the ones place.

3 + 0 + 8 = 11

The next group of important digits are in the tenths place.

1 tenth + 4 tenths + 2 tenths = 7 tenths

Add to make your estimate: 11 + 7 tenths → about 11.7

Estimate each sum.

1. 7.44 + 0.2193

2. 0.4015 + 9.3 + 3.264

3. 0.4208 + 0.16

4. 0.52 + 0.1 + 0.308 + 0.0294

5. 10.2 + 0.519

6. 12.004 + 1.5 + 4.32 + 0.1009

7. 6.72 + 0.5037

8. 0.805 + 1.006 + 0.4 + 2.0305

9. 1.208 + 3.1 + 0.04 + 6.143 + 0.3075

10. 0.9005 + 5.03 + 7.108 + 0.004 + 10.7

This same method works when you need to estimate a sum of much greater numbers. Estimate each sum.

11. 53,129 + 420,916

12. 6,048 + 2,137 + 509

13. 723 + 4,106 + 4,051 + 318

14. 7,095 + 12,402 + 3,114 + 360

15. 650,129 + 22,018 + 107,664 + 10,509

Enrichment Worksheet 3-6

Horizontal Front-End Estimation

Many times an addition problem is given to you in *horizontal form*, with the addends written from left to right. To estimate the sum, you don't have to rewrite the addition vertically in order to line up the decimal points. Just use place value to figure out which digits are most important. Here is an example.

3.11 + 0.4639 + 8.205

The most important digits are in the ones place.

3 + 0 + 8 = 11

The next group of important digits are in the tenths place.

1 tenth + 4 tenths + 2 tenths = 7 tenths

Add to make your estimate: 11 + 7 tenths → about 11.7

Estimate each sum.

1. 7.44 + 0.2193
   about 7.6

2. 0.4015 + 9.3 + 3.264
   about 12.9

3. 0.4208 + 0.16
   about 0.58

4. 0.52 + 0.1 + 0.308 + 0.0294
   about 0.94

5. 10.2 + 0.519
   about 10.7

6. 12.004 + 1.5 + 4.32 + 0.1009
   about 17.9

7. 6.72 + 0.5037
   about 7.2

8. 0.805 + 1.006 + 0.4 + 2.0305
   about 4.2

9. 1.208 + 3.1 + 0.04 + 6.143 + 0.3075
   about 10.7

10. 0.9005 + 5.03 + 7.108 + 0.004 + 10.7
    about 23.7

This same method works when you need to estimate a sum of much greater numbers. Estimate each sum.

11. 53,129 + 420,916   **about 470,000**

12. 6,048 + 2,137 + 509   **about 8,600**

13. 723 + 4,106 + 4,051 + 318   **about 9,100**

14. 7,095 + 12,402 + 3,114 + 360   **about 22,800**

15. 650,129 + 22,018 + 107,664 + 10,509   **about 780,000**

Enrichment Worksheet 3-7

How Much Change?

When you pay for an item in a store, you need to recognize
quickly if you have received the right amount of change.
Here is how estimation can help you.

You gave the clerk: $40.00
Amount of your purchase: $23.15 ⟶ about $23
Change received: $6.85 ⟶ about $7

The sum is only $30. You gave the clerk $40, so the amount
of change is not reasonable.

Circle the amount of change that is most reasonable.

1. The amount of your purchase is $6.74,
   and you give the clerk $20.

   $3.26 $4.26 $13.26 $14.26

2. The cost of dinner is $21.15, and you
   give the server $25.

   $3.15 $3.85 $4.85 $8.85

3. The amount of your purchase is
   $1.89, and you give the clerk $5.

   $4.11 $3.89 $3.11 $2.11

4. You are purchasing a box of cereal
   that costs $3.19 and a roast that costs
   $7.98, and you give the cashier $20.

   $17.81 $12.02 $9.83 $8.83

Make a reasonable estimate of the amount of change.

5. The amount of your purchase is $33.25, and you give the
   clerk two $20 bills.

6. You order a hamburger that costs $2.19, French fries that cost
   $1.15, and milk that costs $0.79. You give the cashier $10.

7. You are purchasing a cassette that costs $5.98 and headphones
   that cost $7.98. You give the clerk a $10 bill and a $5 bill.

8. You are purchasing two sweaters that cost $17.99 each and a
   skirt that costs $21.99. You give the salesperson three $20 bills.

Enrichment Worksheet 3-7

How Much Change?

When you pay for an item in a store, you need to recognize quickly if you have received the right amount of change. Here is how estimation can help you.

> You gave the clerk: $40.00
> Amount of your purchase: $23.15 $\longrightarrow$ about $23
> Change received: $6.85 $\longrightarrow$ about $7
>
> The sum is only $30. You gave the clerk $40, so the amount of change is not reasonable.

Circle the amount of change that is most reasonable.

1. The amount of your purchase is $6.74, and you give the clerk $20.

   $3.26 $4.26   ($13.26) $14.26

2. The cost of dinner is $21.15, and you give the server $25.

   $3.15   ($3.85) $4.85 $8.85

3. The amount of your purchase is $1.89, and you give the clerk $5.

   $4.11 $3.89   ($3.11) $2.11

4. You are purchasing a box of cereal that costs $3.19 and a roast that costs $7.98, and you give the cashier $20.

   $17.81 $12.02 $9.83   ($8.83)

Make a reasonable estimate of the amount of change.

5. The amount of your purchase is $33.25, and you give the clerk two $20 bills.
   about $7

6. You order a hamburger that costs $2.19, French fries that cost $1.15, and milk that costs $0.79. You give the cashier $10.
   about $6

7. You are purchasing a cassette that costs $5.98 and headphones that cost $7.98. You give the clerk a $10 bill and a $5 bill.
   about $1

8. You are purchasing two sweaters that cost $17.99 each and a skirt that costs $21.99. You give the salesperson three $20 bills.
   about $2

Name ______________________ Date ____________

Enrichment Worksheet 3-8

Palindromes

A **palindrome** is a number that reads the same from left to right and from right to left. Decimals like 4.4 and 73.37 are examples of palindromes. A decimal like 5.14 is not a palindrome, of course, but it can be transformed into one using this trick.

Write the number.	5.14	← Be sure to line up the decimal points.
"Flip it" around the decimal point.	+41.5	
Add.	46.64	

Use the addition trick shown above to transform each number into a palindrome.

1. 41.22 **2.** 50.9 **3.** 1.092 **4.** 0.0008

Use two additions to transform each number into a palindrome. (Exercise 5 has been started for you.)

5. 25.61
+16.52
42.13
+31.24

6. 5.92 **7.** 3.904 **8.** 415.9

Transform each number into a palindrome, using as many additions as necessary.

9. 49.6 **10.** 8.9 **11.** 517.6 **12.** 6.58

13. ***CHALLENGE*** Words can be palindromes, too, when they read the same from left to right and from right to left. Can you think of two words that are palindromes?

Glencoe Division, Macmillan/McGraw-Hill

Enrichment Worksheet 3-8

Palindromes

A **palindrome** is a number that reads the same from left to right and from right to left. Decimals like 4.4 and 73.37 are examples of palindromes. A decimal like 5.14 is not a palindrome, of course, but it can be transformed into one using this trick.

Write the number.   5.14 ← Be sure to line
"Flip it" around the decimal point. +41.5   up the decimal points.
Add.
                             46.64

Use the addition trick shown above to transform each number into a palindrome.

1. 41.22   **2.** 50.9   **3.** 1.092   **4.** 0.0008
    63.36   **59.95**   **291.192**   **8,000.0008**

*Use **two** additions to transform each number into a palindrome. (Exercise 5 has been started for you.)*

5.   25.61   **6.** 5.92   **7.** 3.904   **8.** 415.9
      +16.52   **59.95**   **815.518**   **839.938**

       42.13
      +31.24

    73.37

Transform each number into a palindrome, using as many additions as necessary.

9. 49.6   **10.** 8.9   **11.** 517.6   **12.** 6.58
   193.391   **73.37**   **8,321.1238**   **24,503.30542**

13. *CHALLENGE*   Words can be palindromes, too, when they read the same from left to right and from right to left. Can you think of two words that are palindromes?
    Answers will vary. Samples: NOON, RADAR

Enrichment Worksheet 3-9

A Circle Graph Mystery

The circle graph below was drawn to show the leading causes of fire in the United States. However, all the labels except one have mysteriously disappeared.

Use the clues below to decide what the labels should be and where they belong. Then complete the graph. (Remember: Each label must include a word and a decimal.)

Causes of Fires

cooking
0.16

Clue 1 Most fires are caused by *heating equipment*.

Clue 2 Fires caused by *electrical wiring* and fires caused by *heating equipment* together make up 0.46 of all fires.

Clue 3 The part of fires caused by *children playing* is 0.12 less than the part of fires caused by *cooking*.

Clue 4 The part of fires caused by *open flames* is equal to the part of fires caused by *children playing*.

Clue 5 The part of fires caused by *cooking* and the part of fires caused by *arson* are together just 0.01 less than the part of fires caused by *heating equipment*.

Clue 6 The part of fires caused by *electrical wiring* is 0.15 greater than the part caused by *children playing*.

Clue 7 Fires caused by *smoking* and fires caused by *arson* together make up 0.17 of all fires.

Clue 8 Fires that result from other causes are listed in a category called *other*.

Enrichment Worksheet 3-9

A Circle Graph Mystery

The circle graph below was drawn to show the leading causes of fire in the United States. However, all the labels except one have mysteriously disappeared.

Use the clues below to decide what the labels should be and where they belong. Then complete the graph. (Remember: Each label must include a word and a decimal.)

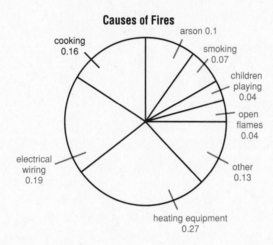

Causes of Fires

arson 0.1
smoking 0.07
children playing 0.04
open flames 0.04
other 0.13
heating equipment 0.27
electrical wiring 0.19
cooking 0.16

Clue 1   Most fires are caused by *heating equipment*.

Clue 2   Fires caused by *electrical wiring* and fires caused by *heating equipment* together make up 0.46 of all fires.

Clue 3   The part of fires caused by *children playing* is 0.12 less than the part of fires caused by *cooking*.

Clue 4   The part of fires caused by *open flames* is equal to the part of fires caused by *children playing*.

Clue 5   The part of fires caused by *cooking* and the part of fires caused by *arson* are together just 0.01 less than the part of fires caused by *heating equipment*.

Clue 6   The part of fires caused by *electrical wiring* is 0.15 greater than the part caused by *children playing*.

Clue 7   Fires caused by *smoking* and fires caused by *arson* together make up 0.17 of all fires.

Clue 8   Fires that result from other causes are listed in a category called *other*.

Enrichment Worksheet 3-10

Magic Squares

A **magic square** is a square arrangement of numbers in which the sum of the numbers in every row, column, and diagonal is the same number. The sum is called the **magic constant**. In the 3-by-3 magic square at the right, the magic constant is 15.

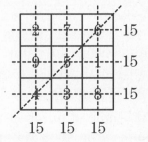

All kinds of numbers are used in magic squares, but something special happens when you use just the counting numbers, starting with 1. In this type of square, called a *normal* magic square, the magic constant is found using this formula.

constant = $n \times (n^2 + 1) \div 2$ ⟵ n^2 means $n \times n$.

In the formula, the variable n represents the number of rows and columns. At the right, you see how to use the formula to find the magic constant for the normal magic square shown above.

$n = 3$
$$\begin{aligned}
\text{constant} &= 3 \times (3^2 + 1) \div 2 \\
&= 3 \times (9 + 1) \div 2 \\
&= 3 \times 10 \div 2 \\
&= 30 \div 2 \\
&= 15
\end{aligned}$$

Each of the following is a <u>normal</u> magic square. Use the magic constant, 15, to complete each square.

1.

	5	
8		4

2.

	9	
3		
	1	

3.

	1	
3		7

4. Use the formula given above. What is the magic constant for a 4-by-4 normal magic square?

Use your answer to Exercise 4 to complete each of these normal magic squares.

5.

4			1
9		7	
	10	11	
			13

6.

		5	8
3			2
		1	14
6			7

7.

7			11
			8
	4	16	
6			10

Enrichment Worksheet 3-10

Magic Squares

A **magic square** is a square arrangement of numbers in which the sum of the numbers in every row, column, and diagonal is the same number. The sum is called the **magic constant**. In the 3-by-3 magic square at the right, the magic constant is 15.

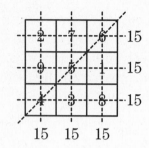

All kinds of numbers are used in magic squares, but something special happens when you use just the counting numbers, starting with 1. In this type of square, called a *normal* magic square, the magic constant is found using this formula.

constant = $n \times (n^2 + 1) \div 2$ ⟵—— n^2 means $n \times n$.

In the formula, the variable n represents the number of rows and columns. At the right, you see how to use the formula to find the magic constant for the normal magic square shown above.

$n = 3$
constant = $3 \times (3^2 + 1) \div 2$
= $3 \times (9 + 1) \div 2$
= $3 \times 10 \div 2$
= $30 \div 2$
= 15

Each of the following is a __normal__ magic square. Use the magic constant, 15, to complete each square.

1.
6	7	2
1	5	9
8	3	4

2.
4	9	2
3	5	7
8	1	6

3.
8	1	6
3	5	7
4	9	2

4. Use the formula given above. What is the magic constant for a 4-by-4 normal magic square?   **34**

Use your answer to Exercise 4 to complete each of these normal magic squares.

5.
4	15	14	1
9	6	7	12
5	10	11	8
16	3	2	13

6.
10	5	8	11
3	16	13	2
15	4	1	14
6	9	12	7

7.
7	14	2	11
12	1	13	8
9	4	16	5
6	15	3	10

Glencoe Division, Macmillan/McGraw-Hill

Enrichment Worksheet 4-1

Job Hunting

Have you ever read the classified ads in a newspaper? If you have, you know that jobs are advertised in a number of ways. For example, the work hours might be described as hours per day or as days per week. The pay might be given as either an hourly or weekly rate.

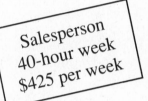

Six people - Elaine, Josita, Lisa, Mark, Steven, and Tran - have each applied for one of the jobs described in the ads on this page. Some clues are given below. Use your estimation and problem solving skills to figure out which job each person is considering. When you feel sure you have found a match, write the person's name next to the job ad.

1. Lisa estimates that, if she gets this job, she can earn about $8,000 in one year.

2. Mark estimates that this job will pay him just less than $280 per week.

3. Elaine figures that, in one year at this job, she can earn just a little more than the $10,000 she needs to pay her tuition.

4. Tran estimates that, in one month at this job, he would earn just a little less than he needs to repay a $500 loan.

5. If she works at this job for three months, Josita estimates that she can earn about $5,000.

6. Steven figures that his earnings from this job will be between $200 and $240 per week.

Salesperson
40-hour week
$425 per week

Baker
Monday-Friday
8-hour day
$6.75 per hour

Housekeeper
6 days per week
40-hour week
$5.50 per hour

Office Manager
Monday-Thursday
9:00 A.M.-2:00 P.M.
$7.75 per hour

Data Processor
20 hours per week
$5.75 per hour

Proofreader
3 days per week
$200 per week

Enrichment Worksheet 4-1

Job Hunting

Have you ever read the classified ads in a newspaper? If you have, you know that jobs are advertised in a number of ways. For example, the work hours might be described as hours per day or as days per week. The pay might be given as either an hourly or weekly rate.

Six people - Elaine, Josita, Lisa, Mark, Steven, and Tran - have each applied for one of the jobs described in the ads on this page. Some clues are given below. Use your estimation and problem solving skills to figure out which job each person is considering. When you feel sure you have found a match, write the person's name next to the job ad.

1. Lisa estimates that, if she gets this job, she can earn about $8,000 in one year.

2. Mark estimates that this job will pay him just less than $280 per week.

3. Elaine figures that, in one year at this job, she can earn just a little more than the $10,000 she needs to pay her tuition.

4. Tran estimates that, in one month at this job, he would earn just a little less than he needs to repay a $500 loan.

5. If she works at this job for three months, Josita estimates that she can earn about $5,000.

6. Steven figures that his earnings from this job will be between $200 and $240 per week.

Salesperson
40-hour week
$425 per week
Josita

Baker
Monday-Friday
8-hour day
$6.75 per hour
Mark

Housekeeper
6 days per week
40-hour week
$5.50 per hour

Steven

Office Manager
Monday-Thursday
9:00 A.M.-2:00 P.M.
$7.75 per hour
Lisa

Tran

Data Processor
20 hours per week
$5.75 per hour

Proofreader
3 days per week
$200 per week
Elaine

Enrichment Worksheet 4-2

Making Models for Numbers

Have you wondered why we read the number 3^2 as *three squared*? The reason is that a common **model** for 3^2 is a square with sides of length 3 units. As you see, the figure that results is made up of 9 *square units*.

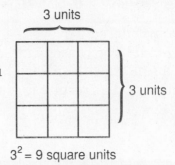

3 units

3 units

$3^2 = 9$ square units

Make a model for each expression.

1. 2^2 **2.** 4^2 **3.** 1^2 **4.** 5^2

Since we read the expression 2^3 as *two cubed,* you probably have guessed that there is also a model for this number. The model, shown at the right, is a cube with sides of length 2 units. The figure that results is made up of 8 *cubic units*.

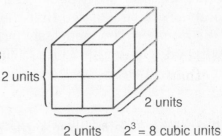

2 units

2 units

2 units $2^3 = 8$ cubic units

Exercises 5 and 6 refer to the figure at the right.

5. What expression is being modeled?

6. Suppose that the entire cube is painted red. Then the cube is cut into small cubes along the lines shown.

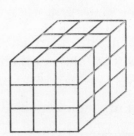

   a. How many small cubes are there in all?

   b. How many small cubes have red paint on exactly three of their faces?

   c. How many small cubes have red paint on exactly two of their faces?

   d. How many small cubes have red paint on exactly one face?

   e. How many small cubes have no red paint at all?

7. *CHALLENGE* In the space at the right, draw a model for the expression 4^3.

Enrichment Worksheet 4-2

Making Models for Numbers

Have you wondered why we read the number 3^2 as *three squared*? The reason is that a common **model** for 3^2 is a square with sides of length 3 units. As you see, the figure that results is made up of 9 *square units*.

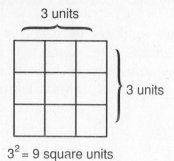

3 units

3 units

$3^2 = 9$ square units

Make a model for each expression.

1. 2^2 **2.** 4^2 **3.** 1^2 ☐   **4.** 5^2

Since we read the expression 2^3 as *two cubed,* you probably have guessed that there is also a model for this number. The model, shown at the right, is a cube with sides of length 2 units. The figure that results is made up of 8 *cubic units*.

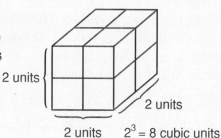

2 units

2 units

2 units $2^3 = 8$ cubic units

Exercises 5 and 6 refer to the figure at the right.

5. What expression is being modeled?   **3^3**

6. Suppose that the entire cube is painted red. Then the cube is cut into small cubes along the lines shown.

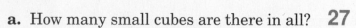

a. How many small cubes are there in all?   **27**

b. How many small cubes have red paint on exactly three of their faces?   **8**

c. How many small cubes have red paint on exactly two of their faces?   **12**

d. How many small cubes have red paint on exactly one face?   **6**

e. How many small cubes have no red paint at all?   **1**

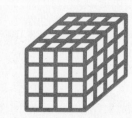

7. **CHALLENGE** In the space at the right, draw a model for the expression 4^3.

Enrichment Worksheet 4-3

Multiplying by 10, 100, and 1,000

Can you see a pattern in these multiplications?

5.931	5.931	5.931
$\times$ 10	$\times$ 100	$\times$ 1,000
59.310 = 59.31	593.100 = 593.1	5,931.000 = 5,931

When you multiply a number by 10, 100, or 1,000, the product contains the same digits as the original number. However, the decimal point "moves" according to these rules:

multiply by 10 ⟶ move to the right one place
multiply by 100 ⟶ move to the right two places
multiply by 1,000 ⟶ move to the right three places

Many people use this fact as a mental math strategy.

Find each product mentally.

1. 10×7.402

2. 100×7.402

3. $1,000 \times 7.402$

4. 10×0.84

5. $1,000 \times 0.5362$

6. 100×3.83

7. 24.07×10

8. $1.918 \times 1,000$

9. 0.075×100

10. 6.1×10

11. 0.0046×100

12. $0.005 \times 1,000$

Now you can use this mental math strategy to estimate some products. The secret is to recognize when one of the factors is fairly close to 10, 100, or 1,000. An example is shown at the right.

32.83	⟶	32.83
$\times$ 97	⟶	$\times$ 100
		3,283

So, 32.83×97 is about 3,283.

Estimate by rounding one number to 10, 100, or 1,000.

13. 6.57×9

14. 14.32×96

15. $1,225 \times 3.548$

16. 0.6214×11.05

17. 98.04×26.331

18. 0.0358×9.3145

19. CHALLENGE Find the product $1,000 \times 16.5$ mentally. How is this different from the other exercises on this page?

Enrichment Worksheet 4-3

Multiplying by 10, 100, and 1,000

Can you see a pattern in these multiplications?

5.931	5.931	5.931
× 10	× 100	× 1,000
59.310 = 59.31	593.100 = 593.1	5,931.000 = 5,931

When you multiply a number by 10, 100, or 1,000, the product contains the same digits as the original number. However, the decimal point "moves" according to these rules:

> multiply by 10 ———→ move to the right one place
> multiply by 100 ———→ move to the right two places
> multiply by 1,000 —→ move to the right three places

Many people use this fact as a mental math strategy.

Find each product mentally.

1. 10×7.402 **74.02**

2. 100×7.402 **740.2**

3. $1,000 \times 7.402$ **7,402**

4. 10×0.84 **8.4**

5. $1,000 \times 0.5362$ **536.2**

6. 100×3.83 **383**

7. 24.07×10 **240.7**

8. $1.918 \times 1,000$ **1,918**

9. 0.075×100 **7.5**

10. 6.1×10 **61**

11. 0.0046×100 **0.46**

12. $0.005 \times 1,000$ **5**

Now you can use this mental math strategy to estimate some products. The secret is to recognize when one of the factors is fairly close to 10, 100, or 1,000. An example is shown at the right.

32.83	⟶	32.83
× 97	⟶	× 100
		3,283

So, 32.83×97 is about 3,283.

Estimate by rounding one number to 10, 100, or 1,000.

13. 6.57×9 **65.7**

14. 14.32×96 **1,432**

15. $1,225 \times 3.548$ **3,548**

16. 0.6214×11.05 **6.214**

17. 98.04×26.331 **2,633.1**

18. 0.0358×9.3145 **0.358**

19. *CHALLENGE* Find the product $1,000 \times 16.5$ mentally. How is this different from the other exercises on this page? **16,500; You must annex some zeros.**

Enrichment Worksheet 4-4

Modeling the Distributive Property

Just as you can model numbers, you can also model operations.
For example, here is a model of the operations in the
distributive property:

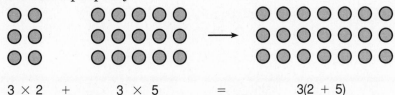

$$3 \times 2 \quad + \quad 3 \times 5 \quad = \quad 3(2 + 5)$$

Write a distributive property statement for each model.

1.

2.

Make a model for each statement.

3. $2 \times 4 + 2 \times 5 = 2(4 + 5)$ **4.** $6(1 + 4) = 6 \times 1 + 6 \times 4$

Write a statement for each model.

5.   6.

7.

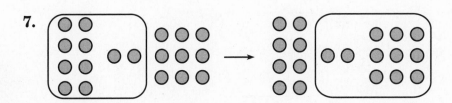

Enrichment Worksheet 4-4

Modeling the Distributive Property

Just as you can model numbers, you can also model operations.
For example, here is a model of the operations in the
distributive property:

3×2 + 3×5 = $3(2 + 5)$

Write a distributive property statement for each model.

1.

$4 \times 3 + 4 \times 2 = 4(3 + 2)$

2.

$2(4 + 7) = 2 \times 4 + 2 \times 7$

Make a model for each statement.

3. $2 \times 4 + 2 \times 5 = 2(4 + 5)$

4. $6(1 + 4) = 6 \times 1 + 6 \times 4$

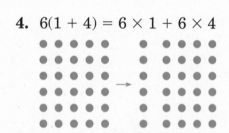

Write a statement for each model.

5.

$2 \times 3 + 4 \times 2 =$
$4 \times 2 + 2 \times 3$

6.

$3 \times 4 = 4 \times 3$

7.

$(4 \times 2 + 1 \times 2) + 3 \times 3 = 4 \times 2 + (1 \times 2 + 3 \times 3)$

Glencoe Division, Macmillan/McGraw-Hill

Enrichment Worksheet 4-5

A Logic Puzzle

Here is a puzzle that will help you brush up on your logical thinking skills.

Example

The product 3.3×8.1 is in both the circle and the triangle, but not in the square. Place the product in the diagram at the right.

$$
\begin{array}{r}
8.1 \\
\times\ 3.3 \\
\hline
243 \\
243 \\
\hline
26.73
\end{array}
$$

Write 26.73 in the ← correct region of the diagram.

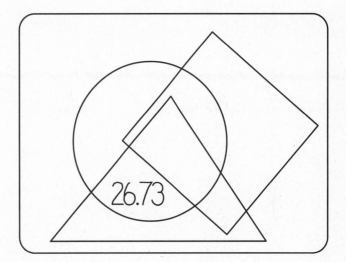

Use the given information to place the product in the diagram at the right.

1. The product 14.19×1.3 is in both the triangle and the square, but not in the circle.

2. The product 0.08×2.7 is in the triangle, but not in the circle or the square.

3. The product 1.24×0.16 is not in the circle, the square, or the triangle.

4. The product 2.2×0.815 is in both the square and the circle, but not in the triangle.

5. The product 0.02×0.03 is in the circle, but not the triangle or the square.

6. The product 21.7×0.95 is in the circle, the square, and the triangle.

7. The product 2.5×12.8 is in the square, but not the circle or triangle.

8. If you did all the calculations correctly, the sum of all the numbers in the diagram should be a "nice" number. What is the sum?

Enrichment Worksheet 4-5

A Logic Puzzle

Here is a puzzle that will help you brush up on your
logical thinking skills.

Example

The product 3.3 × 8.1 is in both the
circle and the triangle, but not in the
square. Place the product in the
diagram at the right.

$$
\begin{array}{r}
8.1 \\
\times\ 3.3 \\
\hline
243 \\
243 \\
\hline
26.73
\end{array}
$$

Write 26.73 in the
← correct region of
the diagram.

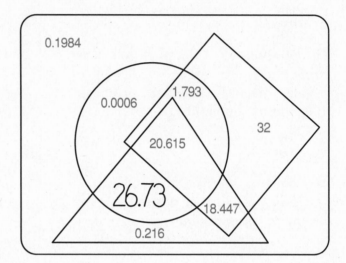

Use the given information to place the product in the diagram at the right.

1. The product 14.19 × 1.3 is in both the triangle and the square, but not in the circle.

2. The product 0.08 × 2.7 is in the triangle, but not in the circle or the square.

3. The product 1.24 × 0.16 is not in the circle, the square, or the triangle.

4. The product 2.2 × 0.815 is in both the square and the circle, but not in the triangle.

5. The product 0.02 × 0.03 is in the circle, but not the triangle or the square.

6. The product 21.7 × 0.95 is in the circle, the square, and the triangle.

7. The product 2.5 × 12.8 is in the square, but not the circle or triangle.

8. If you did all the calculations correctly, the sum of all the numbers in the diagram should be a "nice" number. What is the sum? **100**

Enrichment Worksheet 4-6

Pentominoes

You probably know what a domino looks like. It's simply a plane figure formed by two squares that share a common side. Have you ever heard of a pentomino? A *pentomino* is a plane figure formed by *five* squares, each having at least one side in common with another.

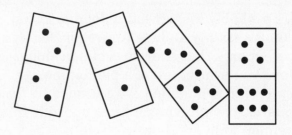

1. These shapes are *not* pentominoes. Can you explain why?
   a.

   b.

2. There are twelve arrangements of five squares that *are* pentominoes. Sketch them in the space below. (The first one is given.)

   (1)   (2)   (3)   (4)

   (5)   (6)   (7)   (8)

   (9)   (10)   (11)   (12)

3. Suppose that the measure of each side of a square is 1 unit. Find the perimeter of each of the twelve pentominoes in Exercise 2.

4. A *hexomino* is formed by six squares. In the space at the right, sketch the hexomino that you think would have the smallest perimeter.

5. **CHALLENGE** Draw the twelve pentominoes on graph paper and cut them out. Using them like pieces of a jigsaw puzzle, arrange them into a rectangle that is 6 units wide and 10 units long.

Enrichment Worksheet 4-6

Pentominoes

You probably know what a domino looks like. It's simply a plane figure formed by two squares that share a common side. Have you ever heard of a pentomino? A *pentomino* is a plane figure formed by *five* squares, each having at least one side in common with another.

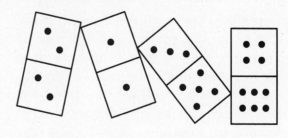

1. These shapes are *not* pentominoes. Can you explain why?

a. **The squares do not share a common side.**

b. **Some squares are joined by only part of a side.**

2. There are twelve arrangements of five squares that *are* pentominoes. Sketch them in the space below. (The first one is given.)

(1)   (2)    (3)   (4)

(5) 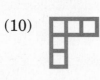   (6) 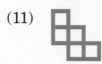   (7)   (8)

(9)   (10)   (11)   (12)

3. Suppose that the measure of each side of a square is 1 unit. Find the perimeter of each of the twelve pentominoes in Exercise 2.

Each pentomino but (5) has a perimeter of 12 units. Pentomino (5) has a perimeter of 10 units.

4. A *hexomino* is formed by six squares. In the space at the right, sketch the hexomino that you think would have the smallest perimeter.

5. *CHALLENGE* Draw the twelve pentominoes on graph paper and cut them out. Using them like pieces of a jigsaw puzzle, arrange them into a rectangle that is 6 units wide and 10 units long. **One arrangement is shown at the right.**

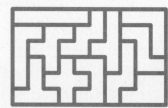

Enrichment Worksheet 4-7

Tiling a Floor

The figure at the right is the floor plan of a family room. The plan is drawn on grid paper, and each square of the grid represents one square foot. The floor is going to be covered completely with tiles.

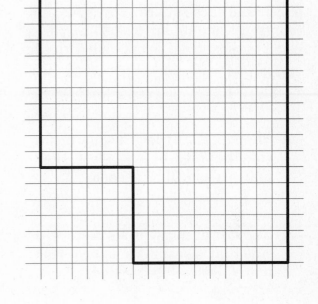

1. What is the area of the floor?

2. Suppose each tile is a square with a side that measures one foot. How many tiles will be needed?

3. Suppose each tile is a square with a side that measures one *inch*. How many tiles will be needed?

4. Suppose each tile is a square with a side that measures six inches. How many tiles will be needed?

Use the given information to find the total cost of tiles for the floor.

5. tile: square, 1 foot by 1 foot
   cost of one tile: $3.50

6. tile: square, 6 inches by 6 inches
   cost of one tile: $0.95

7. tile: square, 4 inches by 4 inches
   cost of one tile: $0.50

8. tile: square, 2 feet by 2 feet
   cost of one tile: $12

9. tile: square, 1 foot by 1 foot
   cost of two tiles: $6.99

10. tile: rectangle, 1 foot by 2 feet
    cost of one tile: $7.99

11. Refer to your answers in Exercises 5-10. Which way of tiling the floor costs the least? the most?

Enrichment Worksheet 4-7

Tiling a Floor

The figure at the right is the floor plan of a family room. The plan is drawn on grid paper, and each square of the grid represents one square foot. The floor is going to be covered completely with tiles.

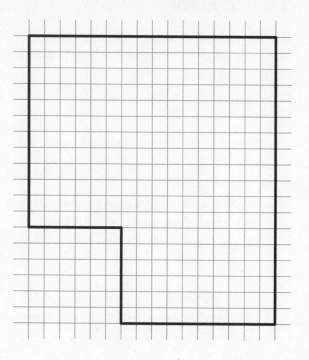

1. What is the area of the floor?
   252 square feet

2. Suppose each tile is a square with a side that measures one foot. How many tiles will be needed?
   252

3. Suppose each tile is a square with a side that measures one *inch*. How many tiles will be needed?
   36,288

4. Suppose each tile is a square with a side that measures six inches. How many tiles will be needed? **1,008**

Use the given information to find the total cost of tiles for the floor.

5. tile: square, 1 foot by 1 foot
   cost of one tile: $3.50
   $882

6. tile: square, 6 inches by 6 inches
   cost of one tile: $0.95
   $957.60

7. tile: square, 4 inches by 4 inches
   cost of one tile: $0.50
   $1,134

8. tile: square, 2 feet by 2 feet
   cost of one tile: $12
   $756

9. tile: square, 1 foot by 1 foot
   cost of two tiles: $6.99
   $880.74

10. tile: rectangle, 1 foot by 2 feet
    cost of one tile: $7.99
    $1,006.74

11. Refer to your answers in Exercises 5-10. Which way of tiling the floor costs the least? the most? **Tiles in Exercise 8: least; Tiles in Exercise 7: most.**

T 35

Enrichment Worksheet 4-8

Checkers, Anyone?

How many squares are on a checkerboard? If you are like most people, your immediate answer is 64. Are you surprised to hear that there are more than 200? To find them all, you must be sure to count all *types* of squares.

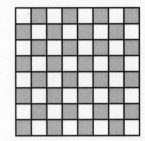

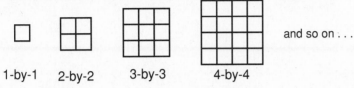

1-by-1   2-by-2   3-by-3   4-by-4   and so on . . .

The questions that follow will show you how to count the squares by solving some simpler problems.

Imagine that there are smaller checkerboards. → Answer these questions for each imaginary checkerboard. ↓	Type of "Checkerboard"			
	2 by 2	3 by 3	4 by 4	5 by 5
1. How many 5-by-5 squares are there?				
2. How many 4-by-4 squares are there?				
3. How many 3-by-3 squares are there?				
4. How many 2-by-2 squares are there?	1			
5. How many 1-by-1 squares are there?	4			

6. What pattern do you see in each column of the table above?

7. Use the pattern that you found in Exercise 6. What numbers would be in a column for the 8-by-8 checkerboard?

8. What is the total number of squares on the 8-by-8 checkerboard?

Glencoe Division, Macmillan/McGraw-Hill

Name _____ **Date** _____

Enrichment Worksheet 4-8

Checkers, Anyone?

How many squares are on a checkerboard? If you are like most people, your immediate answer is 64. Are you surprised to hear that there are more than 200? To find them all, you must be sure to count all *types* of squares.

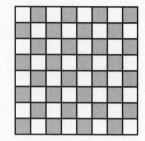

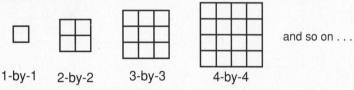

1-by-1   2-by-2   3-by-3   4-by-4   and so on . . .

The questions that follow will show you how to count the squares by solving some simpler problems.

	Imagine that there are smaller checkerboards. → Answer these questions for each imaginary checkerboard. ↓	Type of "Checkerboard"			
		2 by 2	3 by 3	4 by 4	5 by 5
1.	How many 5-by-5 squares are there?				1
2.	How many 4-by-4 squares are there?			1	4
3.	How many 3-by-3 squares are there?		1	4	9
4.	How many 2-by-2 squares are there?	1	4	9	16
5.	How many 1-by-1 squares are there?	4	9	16	25

6. What pattern do you see in each column of the table above?
The numbers are the squares of all the counting numbers up to and including the number of sides.

7. Use the pattern that you found in Exercise 6. What numbers would be in a column for the 8-by-8 checkerboard?
1, 4, 9, 16, 25, 36, 49, and 64

8. What is the total number of squares on the 8-by-8 checkerboard? **204**

T36

Enrichment Worksheet 4-9

Estimating the Area of a Circle

You have learned that area is the number of square units needed to cover a surface. Counting square units on a circular surface can be challenging. Here is a counting method that gives a fairly good *estimate* of the area of a circle.

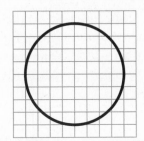

Count the squares that cover any part of the circular region.

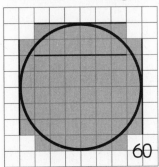

60

Count the squares that are entirely within the circle.

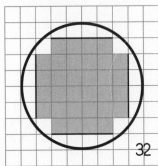

32

Find the mean of the two numbers.
$$\frac{60+32}{2} = \frac{92}{2} = 46$$

So, the area of the circle is about 46 square units.

Estimate the area of each circle or oval.

1.
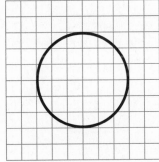

2.
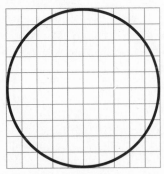

3.
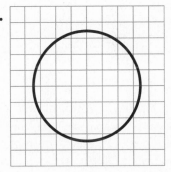

4.
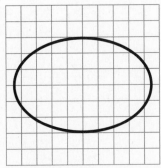

5.
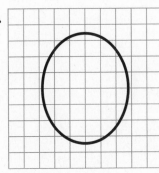

6.
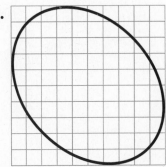

Enrichment Worksheet 4-9

Estimating the Area of a Circle

You have learned that area is the number of square units needed to cover a surface. Counting square units on a circular surface can be challenging. Here is a counting method that gives a fairly good *estimate* of the area of a circle.

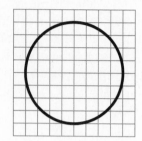

Count the squares that cover any part of the circular region.

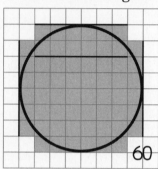

60

Count the squares that are entirely within the circle.

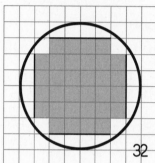

32

Find the mean of the two numbers.
$$\frac{60+32}{2} = \frac{92}{2} = 46$$

So, the area of the circle is about 46 square units. **Estimates of areas may vary. Samples are given.**

Estimate the area of each circle or oval.

1.
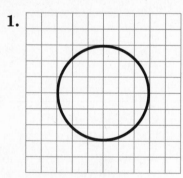

about 26 square units

2.
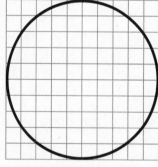

about 74 square units

3.
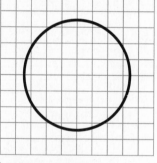

about 38 square units

4.
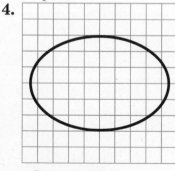

about 42 square units

5.
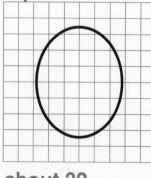

about 32 square units

6.
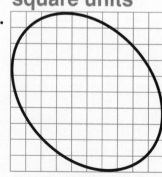

about 69 square units

Glencoe Division, Macmillan/McGraw-Hill

Enrichment Worksheet 5-1

Estimating Quotients

Estimating a quotient is easy when the divisor is near 1, 10, 100, or 1,000. For example, here is how you can estimate $4.08 \div 9.375$.

$4.08 \div 9.375$
9.375 is close to 10.
$4.08 \div 10 = 0.408$ ← Mentally move the decimal point
0.408 is about 0.4   one place to the left.
So $4.08 \div 9.375$ is about 0.4.

Estimate each quotient.

1. $0.684 \div 10.0035$

2. $0.2807 \div 0.94$

3. $22.3 \div 98.05$

4. $6.7 \div 0.9331$

5. $879.4 \div 1,005$

6. $134.038 \div 9.9781$

7. $51.5 \div 0.95$

8. $4,295 \div 992.8$

Another useful skill in estimating quotients is simply recognizing whether the quotient will be greater than 1 or less than 1.

Estimate: $0.5 \div 0.42$

$0.5 > 0.42$, so the quotient will be greater than 1.

Estimate: $4.08 \div 4.35$

$4.08 < 4.35$, so the quotient will be less than 1.

Tell whether each quotient is greater than 1 or less than 1.

9. $0.608 \div 0.695$

10. $0.3009 \div 0.24$

11. $10.482 \div 9.4$

12. $26 \div 25.9007$

13. $0.0084 \div 0.009$

14. $0.005 \div 0.0046$

15. $0.8075 \div 0.81$

16. $9.0049 \div 10.8$

Glencoe Division, Macmillan/McGraw-Hill

Enrichment Worksheet 5-1

Estimating Quotients

Estimating a quotient is easy when the divisor is near 1, 10, 100, or 1,000. For example, here is how you can estimate $4.08 \div 9.375$.

$4.08 \div 9.375$
9.375 is close to 10.
$4.08 \div 10 = 0.408$ ⟵ Mentally move the decimal point
0.408 is about 0.4   one place to the left.
So $4.08 \div 9.375$ is about 0.4.

Estimate each quotient. Estimates may vary.

1. $0.684 \div 10.0035$ about 0.07

2. $0.2807 \div 0.94$ about 0.3

3. $22.3 \div 98.05$ about 0.2

4. $6.7 \div 0.9331$ about 7

5. $879.4 \div 1,005$ about 0.9

6. $134.038 \div 9.9781$ about 13

7. $51.5 \div 0.95$ about 52

8. $4,295 \div 992.8$ about 4.3

Another useful skill in estimating quotients is simply recognizing whether the quotient will be greater than 1 or less than 1.

Estimate: $0.5 \div 0.42$

$0.5 > 0.42$, so the quotient will be greater than 1.

Estimate: $4.08 \div 4.35$

$4.08 < 4.35$, so the quotient will be less than 1.

Tell whether each quotient is greater than 1 or less than 1.

9. $0.608 \div 0.695$ less than 1

10. $0.3009 \div 0.24$ greater than 1

11. $10.482 \div 9.4$ greater than 1

12. $26 \div 25.9007$ greater than 1

13. $0.0084 \div 0.009$ less than 1

14. $0.005 \div 0.0046$ greater than 1

15. $0.8075 \div 0.81$ less than 1

16. $9.0049 \div 10.8$ less than 1

Enrichment Worksheet 5-2

Unit Pricing

The **unit price** of an item is the cost of the item given in terms of one *unit* of the item. The unit might be something that you count, like jars or cans, or it might be a unit of measure, like ounces or pounds. You can find a unit price using this formula.

TUNA
89¢
6-ounce can

$$\begin{array}{r} 0.148 \\ 6\overline{)0.890} \\ \underline{6} \\ 29 \\ \underline{24} \\ 50 \end{array}$$

unit price = cost of item ÷ number of units

For example, you find the unit price of the tuna in the ad at the right by finding the quotient $0.89 \div 6$. The work is shown below the ad. Rounding the quotient to the nearest cent, the unit price is $0.15 *per ounce*.

Find a unit price for each item.

1.
5-pound bag
CARROTS
$1.29

2.
18-ounce jar
PEANUT
BUTTER
$2.49

3.
Grade A Jumbo
EGGS
Dozen
$1.59

Give two different unit prices for each item.

4.
Frozen
BURRITOS
5-ounce pkg
2 for $1.39

5.
Purr-fect
CAT FOOD
3/$1
3-ounce cans

6.
Old Tyme
SPAGHETTI
SAUCE
12-ounce jars
2/$3

Circle the better buy.

7.
Mozarella
Cheese
3/$4
10-ounce pkg

Mozarella
Cheese
2/$3
18-ounce pkg

8.
Dee-light
Chicken
Wings
$9.99
5-pound bag

Top Q
Chicken
Wings
$2.29
18-ounce bag

Glencoe Division, Macmillan/McGraw-Hill

Enrichment Worksheet 5-2

Unit Pricing

The **unit price** of an item is the cost of the item given in terms of one *unit* of the item. The unit might be something that you count, like jars or cans, or it might be a unit of measure, like ounces or pounds. You can find a unit price using this formula.

unit price = cost of item ÷ number of units

For example, you find the unit price of the tuna in the ad at the right by finding the quotient 0.89 ÷ 6. The work is shown below the ad. Rounding the quotient to the nearest cent, the unit price is $0.15 *per ounce*.

TUNA
89¢
6-ounce can

$$\begin{array}{r} 0.148 \\ 6\overline{)0.890} \\ \underline{6} \\ 29 \\ \underline{24} \\ 50 \end{array}$$

Find a unit price for each item.

1.
5-pound bag
CARROTS
$1.29

$0.26 per pound

2.
18-ounce jar
PEANUT
BUTTER
$2.49

$0.14 per ounce

3.
Grade A Jumbo
EGGS
Dozen
$1.59

$0.13 per egg

Give two different unit prices for each item.

4.
Frozen
BURRITOS
5-ounce pkg
2 for $1.39

**$0.70 per package;
$0.14 per ounce**

5.
Purr-fect
CAT FOOD
3/$1
3-ounce cans

**$0.33 per can;
$0.11 per ounce**

6.
Old Tyme
SPAGHETTI
SAUCE
12-ounce jars
2/$3

**$1.50 per jar;
$0.13 per ounce**

Circle the better buy.

7.
Mozarella
Cheese
3/$4
10-ounce pkg

Mozarella
Cheese
2/$3
18-ounce pkg

10-ounce pkg

8.
Dee-light
Chicken
Wings
$9.99
5-pound bag

Top Q
Chicken
Wings
$2.29
18-ounce bag

5-pound bag

Glencoe Division, Macmillan/McGraw-Hill

Name ______________________ Date ______________

Enrichment Worksheet 5-3

Foreign Exchange

The form of money that is used in a country is called the **currency** of that country. The **rate of exchange** tells you what amount of a foreign currency you would receive in exchange for one U.S. dollar. This rate changes daily. The chart at the right shows a few rates of exchange on a recent day. On this day, how many German marks would you get in exchange for $75 (U.S.)?

Multiply: $75 \times 1.6330 = 122.475$
Round to hundredths: 122.48

You would get 122.48 German marks.

Rates of Exchange	
Country (currency)	**Amount per U.S. Dollar**
Britain (pound)	.5737
Canada (dollar)	1.1555
France (franc)	5.3800
Germany (mark)	1.6330
India (rupee)	26.042
Italy (lira)	1218.75
Japan (yen)	129.30
Mexico (peso)	3063.50
Spain (peseta)	101.51
Yugoslavia (dinar)	20.22

Use the chart at the right. Find the amount of each currency that you would receive for $25 (U.S.).

1. marks

2. yen

3. pesos

4. Canadian dollars

To change from an amount of foreign currency to U.S. dollars, you divide. You probably want to use a calculator to find the actual amount, but you can use compatible numbers to make an estimate. At the right you see how to estimate the number of U.S. dollars you would receive for 500 Indian rupees.

500 rupees $\div$ 26.042 = ?

26.042 is about 25.
$500 \div 25 = 20$

So, 500 rupees is about $20.

Use the chart above. Estimate the number of U.S. dollars that you would receive for each amount.

5. 4,500 pesetas

6. 249.8 francs

7. 317 dinars

8. 20,000 lira

9. When traveling in Canada, you find a handbag on sale for $60. You have $50 (U.S.). Do you have enough money?

10. Would you receive a greater amount of U.S. currency in exchange for 100 Canadian dollars or for 100 German marks?

Glencoe Division, Macmillan/McGraw-Hill

Enrichment Worksheet 5-3

Foreign Exchange

The form of money that is used in a country is called the **currency** of that country. The **rate of exchange** tells you what amount of a foreign currency you would receive in exchange for one U.S. dollar. This rate changes daily. The chart at the right shows a few rates of exchange on a recent day. On this day, how many German marks would you get in exchange for $75 (U.S.)?

Multiply: $75 \times 1.6330 = 122.475$
Round to hundredths: 122.48

You would get 122.48 German marks.

Rates of Exchange	
Country (currency)	**Amount per U.S. Dollar**
Britain (pound)	.5737
Canada (dollar)	1.1555
France (franc)	5.3800
Germany (mark)	1.6330
India (rupee)	26.042
Italy (lira)	1218.75
Japan (yen)	129.30
Mexico (peso)	3063.50
Spain (peseta)	101.51
Yugoslavia (dinar)	20.22

Use the chart at the right. Find the amount of each currency that you would receive for $25 (U.S.).

1. marks **40.83**

2. yen **3,232.5**

3. pesos **76,587.5**

4. Canadian dollars **28.89**

To change from an amount of foreign currency to U.S. dollars, you divide. You probably want to use a calculator to find the actual amount, but you can use compatible numbers to make an estimate. At the right you see how to estimate the number of U.S. dollars you would receive for 500 Indian rupees.

500 rupees ÷ 26.042 = ?

26.042 is about 25.
$500 \div 25 = 20$

So, 500 rupees is about $20.

Use the chart above. Estimate the number of U.S. dollars that you would receive for each amount. Estimates may vary.

5. 4,500 pesetas **about $45**

6. 249.8 francs **about $50**

7. 317 dinars **about $15**

8. 20,000 lira **about $20**

9. When traveling in Canada, you find a handbag on sale for $60. You have $50 (U.S.). Do you have enough money?
no

10. Would you receive a greater amount of U.S. currency in exchange for 100 Canadian dollars or for 100 German marks?
100 Canadian dollars

Glencoe Division, Macmillan/McGraw-Hill

Enrichment Worksheet 5-4

It's in the Cards

Below each set of cards, a quotient is given. Use the digits on the cards to form a division sentence with that quotient. Use as many zeros as you need to get the correct number of decimal places. For example, this is how to find a division for the cards at the right.

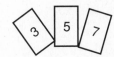

Quotient: 0.0008

You know that $24 \div 3 = 8$.
So, one division is $0.0024 \div 3 = 0.0008$.

1.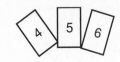

Quotient: 0.009

2.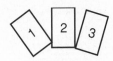

Quotient: 0.04

3.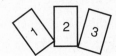

Quotient: 0.0005

4.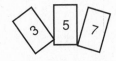

Quotient: 0.0074

5.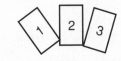

Quotient: 0.0155

6.

Quotient: 0.0025

7.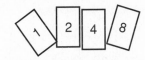

Quotient: 0.0004

8.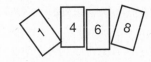

Quotient: 0.03

9.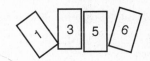

Quotient: 0.005

10.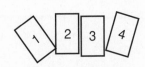

Quotient: 20.65

11.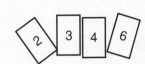

Quotient: 0.0208

12.

Quotient: 0.08

13. **CHALLENGE** Use the cards at the right. Write four *different* divisions that have the quotient 0.4.

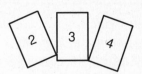

Glencoe Division, Macmillan/McGraw-Hill

Enrichment Worksheet 5-4

It's in the Cards

Below each set of cards, a quotient is given. Use the digits on the cards to form a division sentence with that quotient. Use as many zeros as you need to get the correct number of decimal places. For example, this is how to find a division for the cards at the right.

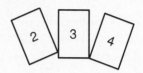

Quotient: 0.0008

You know that 24 ÷ 3 = 8.
So, one division is 0.0024 ÷ 3 = 0.0008. **Answers may vary.**

1.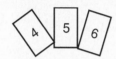

Quotient: 0.009
0.054 ÷ 6

2.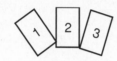

Quotient: 0.04
0.12 ÷ 3

3.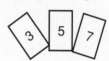

Quotient: 0.0005
0.0035 ÷ 7

4.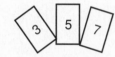

Quotient: 0.0074
0.037 ÷ 5

5.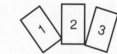

Quotient: 0.0155
0.031 ÷ 2

6.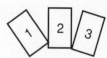

Quotient: 0.0025
0.03 ÷ 12

7.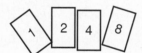

Quotient: 0.0004
0.0048 ÷ 12

8.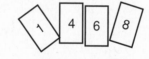

Quotient: 0.03
0.48 ÷ 16

9.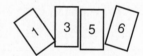

Quotient: 0.005
0.065 ÷ 13

10.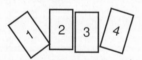

Quotient: 20.65
41.3 ÷ 2

11.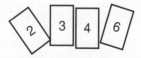

Quotient: 0.0208
0.0624 ÷ 3

12.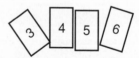

Quotient: 0.08
3.6 ÷ 45

13. **CHALLENGE** Use the cards at the right. Write four *different* divisions that have the quotient 0.4.
**2.4 ÷ 6; 0.24 ÷ 0.6; 0.024 ÷ 0.06;
0.0024 ÷ 0.006**

Enrichment Worksheet 5-5

Length, Mass, or Capacity?

When you encounter a problem about measurement, you won't necessarily see or hear one of the words *length, mass,* or *capacity.* Often you need to decide what type of measurement is involved, then choose the best unit of measure.

Tell whether each question most likely involves length, mass, or capacity.

1. Do I have enough milk to make this recipe?

2. Do I have enough string to tie around this package?

3. Will this punch bowl fit inside that box?

4. Will this amount of punch fit inside that bowl?

5. Is that tunnel high enough for this truck to drive through it?

6. Is that bridge strong enough for this truck to drive over it?

Circle the most reasonable measure for each object.

7. height of a doorway

        2 g   2 kg   2 L   2 mL   2 m   2 cm

8. load limit of an elevator

        1,000 g   1,000 kg   1,000 L   1,000 mL   1,000 m   1,000 cm

9. amount of water in a bathtub

        150 g   1.5 kg   150 L   15 mL   1.5 m   150 cm

10. amount of cereal in a cereal box

        400 g   4 kg   4,000 mL   4 L   0.4 m   400 cm

Name an item that you think has the given measure.

11. about 2 kg

12. about 250 mL

13. about 30 cm

14. about 25 g

42

Enrichment Worksheet 5-5

Length, Mass, or Capacity?

When you encounter a problem about measurement, you won't
necessarily see or hear one of the words *length, mass,* or
capacity. Often you need to decide what type of measurement is
involved, then choose the best unit of measure.

**Tell whether each question most likely involves length, mass,
or capacity.**

1. Do I have enough milk to make this recipe?
   capacity

2. Do I have enough string to tie around this package?
   length

3. Will this punch bowl fit inside that box?
   length

4. Will this amount of punch fit inside that bowl?
   capacity

5. Is that tunnel high enough for this truck to drive through it?
   length

6. Is that bridge strong enough for this truck to drive over it?
   mass

Circle the most reasonable measure for each object.

7. height of a doorway

   2 g   2 kg   2 L   2 mL   (2 m)   2 cm

8. load limit of an elevator

   1,000 g   (1,000 kg)   1,000 L   1,000 mL   1,000 m   1,000 cm

9. amount of water in a bathtub

   150 g   1.5 kg   (150 L)   15 mL   1.5 m   150 cm

10. amount of cereal in a cereal box

    (400 g)   4 kg   4,000 mL   4 L   0.4 m   400 cm

Name an item that you think has the given measure.   Answers will vary.
A sample answer is given.

11. about 2 kg   **textbook**

12. about 250 mL
    small carton of milk

13. about 30 cm   **length of notebook paper**

14. about 25 g   **postage stamp**

T42

Enrichment Worksheet 5-6

Other Metric Units

Meters, millimeters, centimeters, and kilometers are the most commonly used metric units of length. But did you know that there are other units, like *decimeters*, *dekameters*, and *hectometers*? This table shows how all these units are related to the meter.

kilometer (km)	hectometer (hm)	dekameter (dam)	meter (m)	decimeter (dm)	centimeter (cm)	millimeter (mm)
1 km = 1,000 m	1 hm = 100 m	1 dam = 10 m	1 m = 1 m	1 dm = 0.1 m	1 cm = 0.01 m	1 mm = 0.001 m

Each unit in the table is ten times as large as the unit to its right. So, 1 km = 10 hm, and 1 hm = 10 dam. It follows that 1 km = (10 × 10) dam, or 1 km = 100 dam.

Use the chart to complete each statement.

1. 1 dm = _____ cm

2. 1 dm = _____ mm

3. 5 hm = _____ dam

4. 12 km = _____ dam

5. 8.5 km = _____ hm

6. 3.1 dam = _____ dm

7. 1 m = _____ dm = _____ cm = _____ mm

8. 1 km = _____ hm = _____ dam = _____ m

Complete each chart, modeling it on the chart above.

9.

kilogram (kg)			gram (g)			milligram (mg)
1 kg = 1,000 g			1 g = 1 g			1 mg = 0.001 g

10.

			liter (L)			
			1 L = 1 L			

Enrichment Worksheet 5-6

Other Metric Units

Meters, millimeters, centimeters, and kilometers are the most commonly used metric units of length. But did you know that there are other units, like *decimeters*, *dekameters*, and *hectometers*? This table shows how all these units are related to the meter.

kilometer (km)	hectometer (hm)	dekameter (dam)	meter (m)	decimeter (dm)	centimeter (cm)	millimeter (mm)
1 km = 1,000 m	1 hm = 100 m	1 dam = 10 m	1 m = 1 m	1 dm = 0.1 m	1 cm = 0.01 m	1 mm = 0.001 m

Each unit in the table is ten times as large as the unit to its right. So, 1 km = 10 hm, and 1 hm = 10 dam. It follows that 1 km = (10 × 10) dam, or 1 km = 100 dam.

Use the chart to complete each statement.

1. 1 dm = __10__ cm
2. 1 dm = __100__ mm
3. 5 hm = __50__ dam
4. 12 km = __1,200__ dam
5. 8.5 km = __85__ hm
6. 3.1 dam = __310__ dm
7. 1 m = __10__ dm = __100__ cm = __1,000__ mm
8. 1 km = __10__ hm = __100__ dam = __1,000__ m

Complete each chart, modeling it on the chart above.

9.

kilogram (kg)	hectogram (hg)	dekagram (dag)	gram (g)	decigram (dg)	centigram (cg)	milligram (mg)
1 kg = 1,000 g	1 hg = 100 g	1 dag = 10 g	1 g = 1 g	1 dg = 0.1 g	1 cg = 0.01 g	1 mg = 0.001 g

10.

kiloliter (kL)	hectoliter (hL)	dekaliter (daL)	liter (L)	deciliter (dL)	centiliter (cL)	milliliter (mL)
1 kL = 1,000 L	1 hL = 100 L	1 daL = 10 L	1 L = 1 L	1 dL = 0.1 L	1 cL = 0.01 L	1 mL = 0.001 L

Enrichment Worksheet 5-7

Chunking

Have you ever seen an equation like $3(t + 1) = 18$? The expression inside parentheses might make you think that solving this equation is going to be difficult. But, if you can solve $3t = 18$, you probably can solve this equation, too. The trick is to think of the expression $(t + 1)$ as a **chunk**. Here's how.

$$3(t + 1) = 18 \text{ means the same as } \boxed{(t + 1)} = 18 \div 3.$$

$$\boxed{(t + 1)} = 18 \div 3$$

$$\boxed{(t + 1)} = 6$$

You know $5 + 1 = 6$, so $t = 5$.

Solve each equation by chunking.

1. $4(a + 3) = 40$ **2.** $2(m - 5) = 8$ **3.** $3(c - 2) = 18$

4. $25 = 5(z + 4)$ **5.** $14 = 7(k - 4)$ **6.** $20 = 4(x + 1)$

7. $6(1 + x) = 24$ **8.** $3(12 - r) = 30$ **9.** $8(9 + t) = 104$

10. $8 = 8(b - 5)$ **11.** $2(6 - q) = 0$ **12.** $0 = 6(10 - a)$

13. $1.3(x + 1) = 6.5$ **14.** $0.4(j - 9) = 0.8$ **15.** $1.5(k - 6) = 9$

16. $0.2 = 0.05(y + 2)$ **17.** $0.24(d - 5) = 2.16$ **18.** $0.12(e + 2) = 0.36$

Glencoe Division, Macmillan/McGraw-Hill

Enrichment Worksheet 5-7

Chunking

Have you ever seen an equation like $3(t + 1) = 18$? The expression inside parentheses might make you think that solving this equation is going to be difficult. But, if you can solve $3t = 18$, you probably can solve this equation, too. The trick is to think of the expression $(t + 1)$ as a **chunk**. Here's how.

$3(t + 1) = 18$ means the same as $\boxed{(t + 1)} = 18 \div 3$.

$$\boxed{(t + 1)} = 18 \div 3$$

$$\boxed{(t + 1)} = 6$$

You know $5 + 1 = 6$, so $t = 5$.

Solve each equation by chunking.

1. $4(a + 3) = 40$ **7**   **2.** $2(m - 5) = 8$ **9**   **3.** $3(c - 2) = 18$ **8**

4. $25 = 5(z + 4)$ **1**   **5.** $14 = 7(k - 4)$ **6**   **6.** $20 = 4(x + 1)$ **4**

7. $6(1 + x) = 24$ **3**   **8.** $3(12 - r) = 30$ **2**   **9.** $8(9 + t) = 104$ **4**

10. $8 = 8(b - 5)$ **6**   **11.** $2(6 - q) = 0$ **6**   **12.** $0 = 6(10 - a)$ **10**

13. $1.3(x + 1) = 6.5$ **4**   **14.** $0.4(j - 9) = 0.8$ **11**   **15.** $1.5(k - 6) = 9$ **12**

16. $0.2 = 0.05(y + 2)$ **2**   **17.** $0.24(d - 5) = 2.16$ **14**   **18.** $0.12(e + 2) = 0.36$ **1**

Enrichment Worksheet 5-8

Number Puzzles

The puzzles on this page will help you sharpen your arithmetic and logical reasoning skills. Even when you solve a puzzle, you should think about the best method of computation to use— mental math, paper and pencil, or a calculator.

Solve each puzzle. Then identify the method of computation that you think is most appropriate.

1. Arrange the digits 5, 6, 7, 8, and 9 in this multiplication so that you get the greatest possible product.

□ □ □
× □ □
_____

2. Each letter in this addition represents a different digit. What is the value of each letter?

```
  S E N D
+ M O R E
_____
M O N E Y
```

3. Suppose that each equation is true.

$2 ☆ 4 = 10$
$3 ☆ 1 = 10$
$5 ☆ 1 = 6$
$4 ☆ 2 = 14$

What does $8 ☆ 1$ equal?

4. Find the pattern.

$1 × 9 + 2$ = _____

$12 × 9 + 3$ = _____

$123 × 9 + 4$ = _____

$1,234 × 9 + 5$ = _____

What does $12,345,678 × 9 + 9$ equal?

5. Draw two straight lines across the face of this clock so that the sum of the numbers in each region is the same.

6. Arrange the counting numbers from 1 through 6 in the circles so that the sum of the numbers along each side of the triangle is 10.

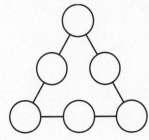

Enrichment Worksheet 5-8

Number Puzzles

The puzzles on this page will help you sharpen your arithmetic and logical reasoning skills. Even when you solve a puzzle, you should think about the best method of computation to use—mental math, paper and pencil, or a calculator.

Solve each puzzle. Then identify the method of computation that you think is most appropriate. **Methods of computation will vary.**

1. Arrange the digits 5, 6, 7, 8, and 9 in this multiplication so that you get the greatest possible product.

$$\boxed{8} \ \boxed{7} \ \boxed{5}$$
$$\times \quad \boxed{9} \ \boxed{6}$$

2. Each letter in this addition represents a different digit. What is the value of each letter?

$$
\begin{array}{r}
\text{S E N D} \\
+ \ \text{M O R E} \\
\hline
\text{M O N E Y}
\end{array}
\qquad
\begin{array}{r}
9{,}567 \\
+ \ 1{,}085 \\
\hline
10{,}652
\end{array}
$$

3. Suppose that each equation is true.

$$2 \ \star \ 4 = 10$$
$$3 \ \star \ 1 = 10$$
$$5 \ \star \ 1 = 16$$
$$4 \ \star \ 2 = 14$$

What does $8 \star 1$ equal? **25**

4. Find the pattern.

$$1 \times 9 + 2 \ = \ \underline{\quad 11 \quad}$$
$$12 \times 9 + 3 \ = \ \underline{\quad 111 \quad}$$
$$123 \times 9 + 4 \ = \ \underline{\quad 1{,}111 \quad}$$
$$1{,}234 \times 9 + 5 \ = \ \underline{\quad 11{,}111 \quad}$$

What does $12{,}345{,}678 \times 9 + 9$ equal?
111,111,111

5. Draw two straight lines across the face of this clock so that the sum of the numbers in each region is the same.

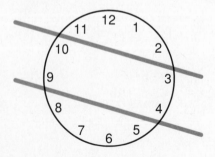

6. Arrange the counting numbers from 1 through 6 in the circles so that the sum of the numbers along each side of the triangle is 10.
Answers will vary.

Enrichment Worksheet 6-1

Leap Years

You probably know that a **leap year** has 366 days, with the extra day being February 29. Did you know that divisibility can help you recognize a leap year? That is because the number of a leap year is always divisible by 4. A number is divisible by 4 if the number formed by its tens and ones digits is divisible by 4.

1936 is divisible by 4 because 36 is divisible by 4.

1938 is not divisible by 4 because 38 is not divisible by 4.

So 1936 was a leap year, and 1938 was not.

Be careful when you decide if a year is a leap year. A century year – like 1800, 1900, or 2000 – is a leap year only if its number is divisible by 400.

Decide whether each year is a leap year. Write yes or no.

1. 1928	**2.** 1930	**3.** 1960	**4.** 1902
5. 1492	**6.** 1776	**7.** 1812	**8.** 1900
9. 1994	**10.** 2000	**11.** 2001	**12.** 2100

13. How many leap years are there between 1901 and 2001?

14. How many leap years were there from the Declaration of Independence in 1776 to the bicentennial celebration in 1976? (Include 1776 and 1976 in your count.)

15. In 1896, the first modern Olympic games were held in Athens, Greece. After that, the officially recognized games were held every four years except for 1916, 1940, and 1944, when the world was at war. How many times were the games held from 1896 to 1992?

16. George Washington was first elected president in 1789. Since 1792, United States presidential elections have been held every four years. How many presidential elections will there have been up to and including the election in the year 2000?

17. *CHALLENGE* If a person lives to be exactly 100 years old, how many leap years or parts of leap years will that person see?

Enrichment Worksheet 6-1

Leap Years

You probably know that a **leap year** has 366 days, with the extra day being February 29. Did you know that divisibility can help you recognize a leap year? That is because the number of a leap year is always divisible by 4. A number is divisible by 4 if the number formed by its tens and ones digits is divisible by 4.

1936 is divisible by 4 because 36 is divisible by 4.

1938 is not divisible by 4 because 38 is not divisible by 4.

So 1936 was a leap year, and 1938 was not.

Be careful when you decide if a year is a leap year. A century year – like 1800, 1900, or 2000 – is a leap year only if its number is divisible by 400.

Decide whether each year is a leap year. Write yes or no.

1. 1928 **yes**　　2. 1930 **no**　　3. 1960 **yes**　　4. 1902 **no**

5. 1492 **yes**　　6. 1776 **yes**　　7. 1812 **yes**　　8. 1900 **no**

9. 1994 **no**　　10. 2000 **yes**　　11. 2001 **no**　　12. 2100 **no**

13. How many leap years are there between 1901 and 2001? **25**

14. How many leap years were there from the Declaration of Independence in 1776 to the bicentennial celebration in 1976? (Include 1776 and 1976 in your count.) **49**

15. In 1896, the first modern Olympic games were held in Athens, Greece. After that, the officially recognized games were held every four years except for 1916, 1940, and 1944, when the world was at war. How many times were the games held from 1896 to 1992? **22**

16. George Washington was first elected president in 1789. Since 1792, United States presidential elections have been held every four years. How many presidential elections will there have been up to and including the election in the year 2000? **54**

17. *CHALLENGE* If a person lives to be exactly 100 years old, how many leap years or parts of leap years will that person see? **24, 25, or 26, depending upon the year of birth.**

Glencoe Division, Macmillan/McGraw-Hill

Enrichment Worksheet 6-2

The Sieve of Erathosthenes

Erathosthenes was a Greek mathematician who lived from about 276 B.C. to 194 B.C. He devised the **Sieve of Erathosthenes** as a method of identifying all the prime numbers up to a certain number. Using the chart below, you can use his method to find all the prime numbers up to 120. Just follow these numbered steps.

1. The number 1 is not prime. Cross it out.

2. The number 2 is prime. Circle it. Then cross out every second number – 4, 6, 8, 10, and so on.

3. The number 3 is prime. Circle it. Then cross out every third number – 6, 9, 12, and so on.

4. The number 4 is crossed out. Go to the next number that is not crossed out.

5. The number 5 is prime. Circle it. Then cross out every fifth number – 10, 15, 20, 25, and so on.

6. Continue crossing out numbers as described in Steps 2–5. The numbers that remain at the end of this process are prime numbers.

7. *CHALLENGE* Look at the prime numbers that are circled in the chart. Do you see a pattern among the prime numbers that are greater than 3? What do you think the pattern is?

1	2	3	4	5	6
7	8	9	10	11	12
13	14	15	16	17	18
19	20	21	22	23	24
25	26	27	28	29	30
31	32	33	34	35	36
37	38	39	40	41	42
43	44	45	46	47	48
49	50	51	52	53	54
55	56	57	58	59	60
61	62	63	64	65	66
67	68	69	70	71	72
73	74	75	76	77	78
79	80	81	82	83	84
85	86	87	88	89	90
91	92	93	94	95	96
97	98	99	100	101	102
103	104	105	106	107	108
109	110	111	112	113	114
115	116	117	118	119	120

Name ______________________ Date ______________

Enrichment Worksheet 6-2

The Sieve of Erathosthenes

Erathosthenes was a Greek mathematician who lived from about 276 B.C. to 194 B.C. He devised the **Sieve of Erathosthenes** as a method of identifying all the prime numbers up to a certain number. Using the chart below, you can use his method to find all the prime numbers up to 120. Just follow these numbered steps.

1. The number 1 is not prime. Cross it out.
2. The number 2 is prime. Circle it. Then cross out every second number – 4, 6, 8, 10, and so on.
3. The number 3 is prime. Circle it. Then cross out every third number – 6, 9, 12, and so on.
4. The number 4 is crossed out. Go to the next number that is not crossed out.
5. The number 5 is prime. Circle it. Then cross out every fifth number – 10, 15, 20, 25, and so on.
6. Continue crossing out numbers as described in Steps 2–5. The numbers that remain at the end of this process are prime numbers.
7. ***CHALLENGE*** Look at the prime numbers that are circled in the chart. Do you see a pattern among the prime numbers that are greater than 3? What do you think the pattern is? **Except for 2 and 3, all prime numbers are of the form 6n+1 or 6n+5.**

~~1~~	②	③	~~4~~	⑤	~~6~~
⑦	~~8~~	~~9~~	~~10~~	⑪	~~12~~
⑬	~~14~~	~~15~~	~~16~~	⑰	~~18~~
⑲	~~20~~	~~21~~	~~22~~	㉓	~~24~~
~~25~~	~~26~~	~~27~~	~~28~~	㉙	~~30~~
㉛	~~32~~	~~33~~	~~34~~	~~35~~	~~36~~
㊲	~~38~~	~~39~~	~~40~~	㊶	~~42~~
㊸	~~44~~	~~45~~	~~46~~	㊼	~~48~~
~~49~~	~~50~~	~~51~~	~~52~~	(53)	~~54~~
~~55~~	~~56~~	~~57~~	~~58~~	(59)	~~60~~
(61)	~~62~~	~~63~~	~~64~~	~~65~~	~~66~~
(67)	~~68~~	~~69~~	~~70~~	(71)	~~72~~
(73)	~~74~~	~~75~~	~~76~~	~~77~~	~~78~~
(79)	~~80~~	~~81~~	~~82~~	(83)	~~84~~
~~85~~	~~86~~	~~87~~	~~88~~	(89)	~~90~~
~~91~~	~~92~~	~~93~~	~~94~~	~~95~~	~~96~~
(97)	~~98~~	~~99~~	~~100~~	(101)	~~102~~
(103)	~~104~~	~~105~~	~~106~~	(107)	~~108~~
(109)	~~110~~	~~111~~	~~112~~	(113)	~~114~~
~~115~~	~~116~~	~~117~~	~~118~~	~~119~~	~~120~~

Glencoe Division, Macmillan/McGraw-Hill

Enrichment Worksheet 6-3

Money Problems

When a problem involves money, you may need to consider both the amount of money and the number of coins or bills involved. Here is an example.

Suppose that you have two dimes and two nickels. How many different amounts can you make with these coins?

To solve the problem, you can make a list like the one at the right. Notice that there are eight different combinations of the coins. However, there are only six different amounts – 5¢, 10¢, 15¢, 20¢, 25¢, and 30¢.

Number of dimes	Number of nickels	Amount
2	0	20¢
2	1	25¢
2	2	30¢
1	0	10¢
1	1	15¢
1	2	20¢
0	1	5¢
0	2	10¢

Solve by making a list.

1. How many different amounts of money can you make with three dimes and three nickels?

2. How many different amounts of money can you make with two $10 bills and three $5 bills?

3. How many different amounts of money can you make with one quarter, one dime, and two nickels?

4. How many different amounts of money can you make with one $20 bill, one $10 bill, and two $5 bills?

5. Using only dimes and nickels, how many different ways can you make change for a dollar?

6. Bus fare is 50¢, and it can only be paid in nickels, dimes, and quarters. How many different ways can you pay the fare?

7. *CHALLENGE* Danny has some coins that amount to more than one dollar, but he still cannot make change for a dollar. What is the greatest number of coins he could have?

Enrichment Worksheet 6-3

Money Problems

When a problem involves money, you may need to consider both the amount of money and the number of coins or bills involved. Here is an example.

Suppose that you have two dimes and two nickels. How many different amounts can you make with these coins?

To solve the problem, you can make a list like the one at the right. Notice that there are eight different combinations of the coins. However, there are only six different amounts – 5¢, 10¢, 15¢, 20¢, 25¢, and 30¢.

Number of dimes	Number of nickels	Amount
2	0	20¢
2	1	25¢
2	2	30¢
1	0	10¢
1	1	15¢
1	2	20¢
0	1	5¢
0	2	10¢

Solve by making a list.

1. How many different amounts of money can you make with three dimes and three nickels? **nine**

2. How many different amounts of money can you make with two $10 bills and three $5 bills? **seven**

3. How many different amounts of money can you make with one quarter, one dime, and two nickels? **nine**

4. How many different amounts of money can you make with one $20 bill, one $10 bill, and two $5 bills? **eight**

5. Using only dimes and nickels, how many different ways can you make change for a dollar? **eleven**

6. Bus fare is 50¢, and it can only be paid in nickels, dimes, and quarters. How many different ways can you pay the fare? **ten**

7. **CHALLENGE** Danny has some coins that amount to more than one dollar, but he still cannot make change for a dollar. What is the greatest number of coins he could have?
fourteen (1 quarter, 9 dimes, 4 pennies)

Enrichment Worksheet 6-4

Perfect!

A **proper factor** of a number is any factor of the number except the number itself. You can use proper factors to classify numbers.

A number is **abundant** if the sum of its proper factors is greater than the number itself.

Proper factors of 12: 1, 2, 3, 4, 6
$1 + 2 + 3 + 4 + 6 = 16$, and $16 > 12$.
So, 12 is *abundant*.

Now you can probably guess the definition of a perfect number. A number is **perfect** if the sum of its proper factors is equal to the number itself.

A number is **deficient** if the sum of its proper factors is less than the number itself.

Proper factors of 16: 1, 2, 4, 8
$1 + 2 + 4 + 8 = 15$, and $15 < 16$.
So, 16 is *deficient*.

Proper factors of 6: 1, 2, 3
$1 + 2 + 3 = 6$
So, 6 is *perfect*!

Tell whether each number is abundant, deficient, or perfect.

1. 8

2. 9

3. 15

4. 18

5. 20

6. 24

7. 25

8. 28

9. 30

10. 35

11. What is the least counting number that is abundant?

12. Is it possible for a prime number to be perfect? Explain.

13. Is it possible for the sum of two deficient numbers to be an abundant number? Explain.

14. *CHALLENGE* Show why 496 is a perfect number.

Enrichment Worksheet 6-4

Perfect!

A **proper factor** of a number is any factor of the number except the number itself. You can use proper factors to classify numbers.

A number is **abundant** if the sum of its proper factors is greater than the number itself.

Proper factors of 12: 1, 2, 3, 4, 6
$1 + 2 + 3 + 4 + 6 = 16$, and $16 > 12$.
So, 12 is *abundant*.

Now you can probably guess the definition of a perfect number. A number is **perfect** if the sum of its proper factors is equal to the number itself.

A number is **deficient** if the sum of its proper factors is less than the number itself.

Proper factors of 16: 1, 2, 4, 8
$1 + 2 + 4 + 8 = 15$, and $15 < 16$.
So, 16 is *deficient*.

Proper factors of 6: 1, 2, 3
$1 + 2 + 3 = 6$
So, 6 is *perfect*!

Tell whether each number is abundant, deficient, or perfect.

1. 8 **deficient**

2. 9 **deficient**

3. 15 **deficient**

4. 18 **abundant**

5. 20 **abundant**

6. 24 **abundant**

7. 25 **deficient**

8. 28 **perfect**

9. 30 **abundant**

10. 35 **deficient**

11. What is the least counting number that is abundant?   **12**

12. Is it possible for a prime number to be perfect? Explain.   **No. The only proper factor of a prime number is 1, so any prime number is deficient.**

13. Is it possible for the sum of two deficient numbers to be an abundant number? Explain. **Yes. Example: 10 (deficient) + 8 (deficient) = 18 (abundant)**

14. *CHALLENGE* Show why 496 is a perfect number.
   $1 + 2 + 4 + 8 + 16 + 31 + 62 + 124 + 248 = 496$

Glencoe Division, Macmillan/McGraw-Hill

Enrichment Worksheet 6-5

Fraction Mysteries

Here is a set of mysteries that will help you sharpen your thinking skills. In each exercise, use the clues to discover the identity of the mystery fraction.

1. My numerator is 6 less than my denominator.

I am equivalent to $\frac{3}{4}$.

2. My denominator is 5 more than twice my numerator.

I am equivalent to $\frac{1}{3}$.

3. The GCF of my numerator and denominator is 3.

I am equivalent to $\frac{2}{5}$.

4. The GCF of my numerator and denominator is 5.

I am equivalent to $\frac{4}{6}$.

5. My numerator and denominator are prime numbers.

My numerator is one less than my denominator.

6. My numerator and denominator are prime numbers.

The sum of my numerator and denominator is 24.

7. My numerator is divisible by 3.

My denominator is divisible by 5.

My denominator is 4 less than twice my numerator.

8. My numerator is divisible by 3.

My denominator is divisible by 5.

My denominator is 3 more than twice my numerator.

9. My numerator is a one-digit prime number.

My denominator is a one-digit composite number.

I am equivalent to $\frac{8}{32}$.

10. My numerator is a prime number.

The GCF of my numerator and denominator is 2.

I am equivalent to $\frac{1}{5}$.

11. CHALLENGE Make up your own mystery like the ones above. Be sure that there is only one solution. To check, have a classmate solve your mystery.

Enrichment Worksheet 6-5

Fraction Mysteries

Here is a set of mysteries that will help you sharpen your thinking skills. In each exercise, use the clues to discover the identity of the mystery fraction.

1. My numerator is 6 less than my denominator.

   I am equivalent to $\frac{3}{4}$. $\frac{18}{24}$

2. My denominator is 5 more than twice my numerator.

   I am equivalent to $\frac{1}{3}$. $\frac{5}{15}$

3. The GCF of my numerator and denominator is 3.

   I am equivalent to $\frac{2}{5}$. $\frac{6}{15}$

4. The GCF of my numerator and denominator is 5.

   I am equivalent to $\frac{4}{6}$. $\frac{10}{15}$

5. My numerator and denominator are prime numbers.

   My numerator is one less than my denominator. $\frac{2}{3}$

6. My numerator and denominator are prime numbers.

   The sum of my numerator and denominator is 24. $\frac{11}{13}$ or $\frac{13}{11}$

7. My numerator is divisible by 3.

   My denominator is divisible by 5.

   My denominator is 4 less than twice my numerator. $\frac{12}{20}$

8. My numerator is divisible by 3.

   My denominator is divisible by 5.

   My denominator is 3 more than twice my numerator. $\frac{6}{15}$

9. My numerator is a one-digit prime number.

   My denominator is a one-digit composite number.

   I am equivalent to $\frac{8}{32}$. $\frac{2}{8}$

10. My numerator is a prime number.

    The GCF of my numerator and denominator is 2.

    I am equivalent to $\frac{1}{5}$. $\frac{2}{10}$

11. **CHALLENGE** Make up your own mystery like the ones above. Be sure that there is only one solution. To check, have a classmate solve your mystery. **Answers will vary.**

Glencoe Division, Macmillan/McGraw-Hill

Enrichment Worksheet 6-6

Nice Fractions

Can fractions be nice? When you see fractions like the
ones at the right, it is hard to think of them as anything
but nasty. Sometimes, all you need to do is write a
simple fraction – a "nice" fraction – as an estimate. You
can do this by using compatible numbers.

$\frac{6}{17} \rightarrow \frac{6}{18}$ ← 17 is close to 18,
$\quad\quad\quad\quad\quad$ and 18 = 3 × 6.

$\frac{6}{18} = \frac{1}{3}$

$\frac{149}{98} \rightarrow \frac{150}{100}$ ← 149 is close to 150.
$\quad\quad\quad\quad\quad\quad$ 98 is close to 100.

$\frac{150}{100} = \frac{3}{2}$

**Choose the best estimate for each fraction from the
choices at the right.**

1. $\frac{15}{21}$

2. $\frac{35}{24}$

3. $\frac{21}{29}$

4. $\frac{24}{49}$

5. $\frac{49}{41}$

6. $\frac{89}{46}$

7. $\frac{59}{48}$

8. $\frac{19}{81}$

9. $\frac{147}{298}$

10. $\frac{118}{61}$

11. $\frac{39}{158}$

12. $\frac{76}{51}$

a. about $\frac{1}{4}$

b. about $\frac{1}{2}$

c. about $\frac{3}{4}$

d. about $1\frac{1}{4}$

e. about $1\frac{1}{2}$

f. about 2

Write a nice fraction as an estimate of each fraction.

13. $\frac{4}{19}$

14. $\frac{12}{25}$

15. $\frac{7}{31}$

16. $\frac{8}{53}$

17. $\frac{14}{25}$

18. $\frac{30}{37}$

19. $\frac{23}{35}$

20. $\frac{79}{98}$

21. $\frac{53}{44}$

22. $\frac{50}{19}$

23. $\frac{121}{79}$

24. $\frac{198}{147}$

Write a fraction that fits each description.

25. It's close to $\frac{1}{2}$.
The denominator is 55.

26. It's close to $\frac{2}{3}$.
The numerator is 99.

27. It's close to $1\frac{1}{2}$.
The denominator is 49.

28. It's close to $\frac{2}{3}$.
The denominator is 89.

Enrichment Worksheet 6-6

Nice Fractions

Can fractions be nice? When you see fractions like the ones at the right, it is hard to think of them as anything but nasty. Sometimes, all you need to do is write a simple fraction – a "nice" fraction – as an estimate. You can do this by using compatible numbers.

$\frac{6}{17} \rightarrow \frac{6}{18}$ ← 17 is close to 18, and 18 = 3 × 6.

$\frac{6}{18} = \frac{1}{3}$

$\frac{149}{98} \rightarrow \frac{150}{100}$ ← 149 is close to 150. 98 is close to 100.

$\frac{150}{100} = \frac{3}{2}$

Choose the best estimate for each fraction from the choices at the right.

1. $\frac{15}{21}$ **c**   2. $\frac{35}{24}$ **e**   3. $\frac{21}{29}$ **c**   4. $\frac{24}{49}$ **b**

5. $\frac{49}{41}$ **d**   6. $\frac{89}{46}$ **f**   7. $\frac{59}{48}$ **d**   8. $\frac{19}{81}$ **a**

9. $\frac{147}{298}$ **b**   10. $\frac{118}{61}$ **f**   11. $\frac{39}{158}$ **a**   12. $\frac{76}{51}$ **e**

a. about $\frac{1}{4}$
b. about $\frac{1}{2}$
c. about $\frac{3}{4}$
d. about $1\frac{1}{4}$
e. about $1\frac{1}{2}$
f. about 2

Write a nice fraction as an estimate of each fraction. **Estimates may vary.**

13. $\frac{4}{19}$ **$\frac{1}{5}$**   14. $\frac{12}{25}$ **$\frac{1}{2}$**   15. $\frac{7}{31}$ **$\frac{1}{4}$ or $\frac{1}{5}$**   16. $\frac{8}{53}$ **$\frac{1}{6}$**

17. $\frac{14}{25}$ **$\frac{3}{5}$**   18. $\frac{30}{37}$ **$\frac{5}{6}$**   19. $\frac{23}{35}$ **$\frac{2}{3}$**   20. $\frac{79}{98}$ **$\frac{4}{5}$**

21. $\frac{53}{44}$ **$\frac{5}{4}$**   22. $\frac{50}{19}$ **$\frac{5}{2}$**   23. $\frac{121}{79}$ **$\frac{3}{2}$**   24. $\frac{198}{147}$ **$\frac{4}{3}$**

Write a fraction that fits each description. **Answers may vary.**

25. It's close to $\frac{1}{2}$. The denominator is 55. **$\frac{27}{55}$ or $\frac{28}{55}$**

26. It's close to $\frac{2}{3}$. The numerator is 99. **$\frac{99}{150}$**

27. It's close to $1\frac{1}{2}$. The denominator is 49. **$\frac{75}{49}$**

28. It's close to $\frac{2}{3}$. The denominator is 89. **$\frac{60}{89}$**

Enrichment Worksheet 6-7

Estimating Lengths

Many people estimate lengths using *rules of thumb* like those you see at the right.

An **inch** is about the width of a quarter.
A **foot** is about the length of a sheet of notebook paper.
A **yard** is about the distance from the floor to a doorknob.
A **mile** is about the length of twenty city blocks.

***Use the rules of thumb to estimate.
Circle the most reasonable measure.***

1. length of a bus	40 in.	40 ft	40 yd
2. length of a baseball bat	15 in.	1 ft	1 yd
3. height of a flagpole	30 in.	3 ft	5 yd
4. height of a table	36 in.	10 ft	2 yd
5. distance across a street	20 ft	200 yd	1 mi
6. length of one city block	30 ft	90 yd	$\frac{1}{2}$ mi
7. width of a door	15 in.	15 ft	1 yd
8. height of the world's tallest building	50 ft	100 yd	$\frac{1}{4}$ mi

9. Estimate the length of the path from **A** to **B**. Then measure. How close was your estimate?

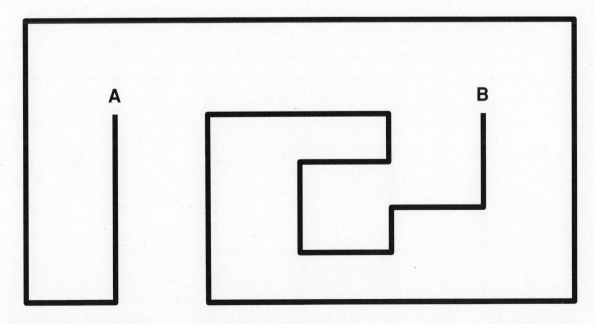

Enrichment Worksheet 6-7

Estimating Lengths

Many people estimate lengths using *rules of thumb* like those you see at the right.

An **inch** is about the width of a quarter.
A **foot** is about the length of a sheet of notebook paper.
A **yard** is about the distance from the floor to a doorknob.
A **mile** is about the length of twenty city blocks.

Use the rules of thumb to estimate.
Circle the most reasonable measure.

1. length of a bus   40 in.   (40 ft)   40 yd

2. length of a baseball bat   15 in.   1 ft   (1 yd)

3. height of a flagpole   30 in.   3 ft   (5 yd)

4. height of a table   (36 in.)   10 ft   2 yd

5. distance across a street   (20 ft)   200 yd   1 mi

6. length of one city block   30 ft   (90 yd) $\frac{1}{2}$ mi

7. width of a door   15 in.   15 ft   (1 yd)

8. height of the world's tallest building   50 ft   100 yd $\left(\frac{1}{4} \text{ mi}\right)$

9. Estimate the length of the path from **A** to **B**. Then measure. How close was your estimate? **Estimates will vary.**
   Length is 29 in.

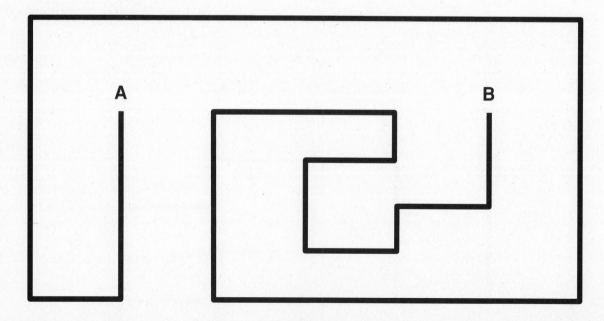

Glencoe Division, Macmillan/McGraw-Hill

Enrichment Worksheet 6-8

Getting From Here to There

At the right, you see a rectangle on a grid of squares. The rectangle is 4 units wide and 7 units long. The *diagonal path* of this rectangle crosses 10 squares of the grid.

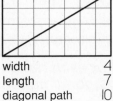

width   4
length   7
diagonal path 10

For each rectangle, record the width, the length, and the diagonal path.

1.    **2.** 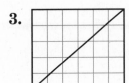   **3.** 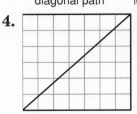   **4.**

5. Refer to your answers to Exercises 1–4. What is the pattern?

Now record the width, length, and diagonal path for each of these rectangles.

6. 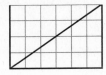   **7.**    **8.**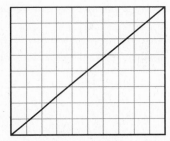

9. Refer to your answers to Exercises 6–8. Does the pattern that you found in Exercise 5 still hold?

10. What is the difference between the rectangles in Exercises 1–4 and the rectangles in Exercises 6–8?

Predict the diagonal path for each rectangle.

11. 4 units by 9 units

12. 10 units by 21 units

13. 20 units by 30 units

14. 20 units by 24 units

Enrichment Worksheet 6-8

Getting From Here to There

At the right, you see a rectangle on a grid of squares. The rectangle is 4 units wide and 7 units long. The *diagonal path* of this rectangle crosses 10 squares of the grid.

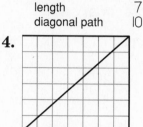

width	4
length	7
diagonal path	10

For each rectangle, record the width, the length, and the diagonal path.

1.

2.

3.

4.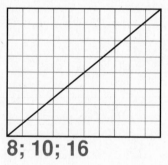

2; 3; 4

3; 4; 6

5; 6; 10

6; 7; 12

5. Refer to your answers to Exercises 1–4. What is the pattern?
The diagonal path is one less than the sum of the width and length.

Now record the width, length, and diagonal path for each of these rectangles.

6.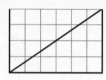

7.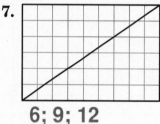

8.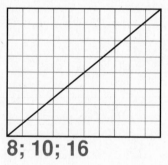

4; 6; 8

6; 9; 12

8; 10; 16

9. Refer to your answers to Exercises 6–8. Does the pattern that you found in Exercise 5 still hold?
no

10. What is the difference between the rectangles in Exercises 1–4 and the rectangles in Exercises 6–8?
In Exercises 1–4, the GCF of the width and length is 1.

Predict the diagonal path for each rectangle.

11. 4 units by 9 units **12**

12. 10 units by 21 units **30**

13. 20 units by 30 units **40**

14. 20 units by 24 units **40**

Enrichment Worksheet 6-9

Developing Fraction Sense

If someone asked you to name a fraction between $\frac{4}{7}$ and $\frac{6}{7}$, you probably would give the answer $\frac{5}{7}$ pretty quickly. But what if you were asked to name a fraction between $\frac{4}{7}$ and $\frac{5}{7}$? At the right, you can see how to approach the problem using "fraction sense." So, one fraction between $\frac{4}{7}$ and $\frac{5}{7}$ is $\frac{9}{14}$.

$$\frac{4}{7} = \frac{\square}{14} \rightarrow \frac{4}{7} = \frac{8}{14}$$

$$\frac{5}{7} = \frac{\square}{14} \rightarrow \frac{5}{7} = \frac{10}{14}$$

Use your fraction sense to solve each problem.

1. Name a fraction between $\frac{1}{3}$ and $\frac{2}{3}$.

2. Name a fraction between $\frac{3}{5}$ and $\frac{4}{5}$.

3. Name five fractions between $\frac{1}{2}$ and 1.

4. Name five fractions between 0 and $\frac{1}{4}$.

5. Name a fraction between $\frac{1}{4}$ and $\frac{1}{2}$ whose denominator is 16.

6. Name a fraction between $\frac{2}{3}$ and $\frac{3}{4}$ whose denominator is 10.

7. Name a fraction between 0 and $\frac{1}{6}$ whose numerator is 1.

8. Name a fraction between 0 and $\frac{1}{10}$ whose numerator is *not* 1.

9. Name a fraction that is halfway between $\frac{2}{9}$ and $\frac{5}{9}$.

10. Name a fraction between $\frac{1}{4}$ and $\frac{3}{4}$ that is closer to $\frac{1}{4}$ than $\frac{3}{4}$.

11. Name a fraction between 0 and $\frac{1}{2}$ that is less than $\frac{3}{10}$.

12. Name a fraction between $\frac{1}{2}$ and 1 that is less than $\frac{3}{5}$.

13. Name a fraction between $\frac{1}{2}$ and $\frac{3}{4}$ that is greater than $\frac{4}{5}$.

14. How many fractions are there between $\frac{1}{4}$ and $\frac{1}{2}$?

Enrichment Worksheet 6-9

Developing Fraction Sense

If someone asked you to name a fraction between $\frac{4}{7}$ and $\frac{6}{7}$, you probably would give the answer $\frac{5}{7}$ pretty quickly. But what if you were asked to name a fraction between $\frac{4}{7}$ and $\frac{5}{7}$? At the right, you can see how to approach the problem using "fraction sense." So, one fraction between $\frac{4}{7}$ and $\frac{5}{7}$ is $\frac{9}{14}$.

$$\frac{4}{7} = \frac{\square}{14} \rightarrow \frac{4}{7} = \frac{8}{14}$$

$$\frac{5}{7} = \frac{\square}{14} \rightarrow \frac{5}{7} = \frac{10}{14}$$

Use your fraction sense to solve each problem.

Answers may vary. Sample answers are given.

1. Name a fraction between $\frac{1}{3}$ and $\frac{2}{3}$.

   $\frac{1}{2}$

2. Name a fraction between $\frac{3}{5}$ and $\frac{4}{5}$.

   $\frac{7}{10}$

3. Name five fractions between $\frac{1}{2}$ and 1. $\frac{2}{3}, \frac{3}{4}, \frac{5}{6}, \frac{7}{8}, \frac{9}{10}$

4. Name five fractions between 0 and $\frac{1}{4}$. $\frac{1}{5}, \frac{1}{6}, \frac{1}{7}, \frac{1}{8}, \frac{1}{9}$

5. Name a fraction between $\frac{1}{4}$ and $\frac{1}{2}$ whose denominator is 16. $\frac{5}{16}$

6. Name a fraction between $\frac{2}{3}$ and $\frac{3}{4}$ whose denominator is 10. $\frac{7}{10}$

7. Name a fraction between 0 and $\frac{1}{6}$ whose numerator is 1. $\frac{1}{7}$

8. Name a fraction between 0 and $\frac{1}{10}$ whose numerator is *not* 1. $\frac{3}{40}$

9. Name a fraction that is halfway between $\frac{2}{9}$ and $\frac{5}{9}$. $\frac{7}{18}$

10. Name a fraction between $\frac{1}{4}$ and $\frac{3}{4}$ that is closer to $\frac{1}{4}$ than $\frac{3}{4}$. $\frac{1}{3}$

11. Name a fraction between 0 and $\frac{1}{2}$ that is less than $\frac{3}{10}$. $\frac{1}{5}$

12. Name a fraction between $\frac{1}{2}$ and 1 that is less than $\frac{3}{5}$. $\frac{11}{20}$

13. Name a fraction between $\frac{1}{2}$ and $\frac{3}{4}$ that is greater than $\frac{4}{5}$.
    There are none.

14. How many fractions are there between $\frac{1}{4}$ and $\frac{1}{2}$?
    There are infinitely many.

Enrichment Worksheet 6-10

Estimating with Decimals and Fractions

Often you only need to give a fractional estimate for a decimal. To make fractional estimates, it helps to become familiar with the fraction-decimal equivalents shown in the chart at the right. You also should be able to identify the fraction as an *overestimate* or *underestimate*. Here's how.

> The decimal 0.789 is a little less than 0.8, so it is a little less than $\frac{4}{5}$. Write $\frac{4^-}{5}$.
>
> The decimal 1.13 is a little more than 1.125, so it is a little more than $1\frac{1}{8}$. Write $1\frac{1}{8}^+$.

Write a fractional estimate for each decimal. Be sure to identify your estimate as an overestimate or an underestimate.

1. 0.243	**2.** 0.509	**3.** 0.429
4. 0.741	**5.** 0.88	**6.** 0.63
7. 0.09	**8.** 0.57	**9.** 1.471
10. 2.76	**11.** 1.289	**12.** 5.218

13. The scale in the delicatessen shows 0.73 pound. Write a fractional estimate for this weight.

14. Darnell ordered a quarter pound of cheese. The scale shows 0.23 pound. Is this more or less than he ordered?

15. On the stock market, prices are listed as halves, fourths, and eighths of a dollar. Yesterday the price of one share of a stock was $25.61. Write a fractional estimate for this amount.

16. Charlotte used a calculator to figure out how many yards of ribbon she needed for a craft project. The display shows 2.53125. Write a fractional estimate for this length.

$0.1 = \frac{1}{10}$	
$0.125 = \frac{1}{8}$	
$0.2 = \frac{1}{5}$	
$0.25 = \frac{1}{4}$	
$0.3 = \frac{3}{10}$	
$0.375 = \frac{3}{8}$	
$0.4 = \frac{2}{5}$	
$0.5 = \frac{1}{2}$	
$0.6 = \frac{3}{5}$	
$0.625 = \frac{5}{8}$	
$0.7 = \frac{7}{10}$	
$0.75 = \frac{3}{4}$	
$0.8 = \frac{4}{5}$	
$0.875 = \frac{7}{8}$	
$0.9 = \frac{9}{10}$	

Enrichment Worksheet 6-10

Estimating with Decimals and Fractions

Often you only need to give a fractional estimate for a decimal. To make fractional estimates, it helps to become familiar with the fraction-decimal equivalents shown in the chart at the right. You also should be able to identify the fraction as an *overestimate* or *underestimate*. Here's how.

The decimal 0.789 is a little less than 0.8, so it is a little less than $\frac{4}{5}$. Write $\frac{4}{5}^-$.

The decimal 1.13 is a little more than 1.125, so it is a little more than $1\frac{1}{8}$. Write $1\frac{1}{8}^+$.

Estimates may vary.

Write a fractional estimate for each decimal. Be sure to identify your estimate as an overestimate or an underestimate.

1. 0.243 $\frac{1}{4}^-$	**2.** 0.509 $\frac{1}{2}^+$	**3.** 0.429 $\frac{2}{5}^+$	
4. 0.741 $\frac{3}{4}^-$	**5.** 0.88 $\frac{7}{8}^+$	**6.** 0.63 $\frac{5}{8}^+$	
7. 0.09 $\frac{1}{10}^-$	**8.** 0.57 $\frac{3}{5}^-$	**9.** 1.471 $1\frac{1}{2}^-$	
10. 2.76 $2\frac{3}{4}^+$	**11.** 1.289 $1\frac{3}{10}^-$	**12.** 5.218 $5\frac{1}{4}^-$	

$$0.1 = \frac{1}{10}$$
$$0.125 = \frac{1}{8}$$
$$0.2 = \frac{1}{5}$$
$$0.25 = \frac{1}{4}$$
$$0.3 = \frac{3}{10}$$
$$0.375 = \frac{3}{8}$$
$$0.4 = \frac{2}{5}$$
$$0.5 = \frac{1}{2}$$
$$0.6 = \frac{3}{5}$$
$$0.625 = \frac{5}{8}$$
$$0.7 = \frac{7}{10}$$
$$0.75 = \frac{3}{4}$$
$$0.8 = \frac{4}{5}$$
$$0.875 = \frac{7}{8}$$
$$0.9 = \frac{9}{10}$$

13. The scale in the delicatessen shows 0.73 pound. Write a fractional estimate for this weight. $\frac{3}{4}$ lb.$^-$

14. Darnell ordered a quarter pound of cheese. The scale shows 0.23 pound. Is this more or less than he ordered? **less**

15. On the stock market, prices are listed as halves, fourths, and eighths of a dollar. Yesterday the price of one share of a stock was $25.61. Write a fractional estimate for this amount. $25 $\frac{5}{8}^-$

16. Charlotte used a calculator to figure out how many yards of ribbon she needed for a craft project. The display shows 2.53125. Write a fractional estimate for this length. $2\frac{1}{2}$ yd$^+$

Enrichment Worksheet 6-11

Tagging Along

Which of $\frac{2}{3}$, $\frac{3}{4}$, $\frac{4}{5}$, and $\frac{9}{10}$ belongs in the "tag" on the number line at the right? The tag is to the right of 0.75, so the fraction must be greater than 0.75. Express each fraction as a decimal.

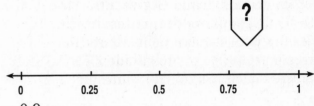

$\frac{2}{3} = 0.\overline{6}$, $\frac{3}{4} = 0.75$, $\frac{4}{5} = 0.8$, $\frac{9}{10} = 0.9$

Only 0.8 and 0.9 are greater than 0.75, and 0.9 is much closer to 1 than to 0.75. Choose 0.8, which is equal to $\frac{4}{5}$.

On each number line, fill in the tags using the given fractions.

1. $\frac{3}{8}$, $\frac{1}{2}$, $\frac{2}{3}$, $\frac{1}{9}$, $\frac{7}{8}$

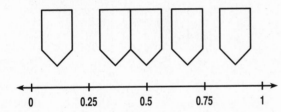

2. $\frac{4}{3}$, $\frac{3}{4}$, $\frac{6}{5}$, $\frac{5}{8}$, $\frac{15}{16}$

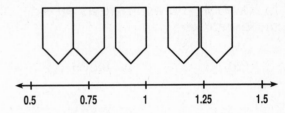

3. $\frac{7}{4}$, $\frac{6}{5}$, $\frac{15}{8}$, $\frac{3}{2}$, $\frac{4}{3}$

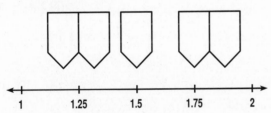

4. $\frac{9}{5}$, $\frac{7}{3}$, $\frac{8}{5}$, $\frac{13}{6}$, $\frac{8}{4}$

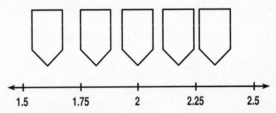

5. Write a fraction in simplest form for each tag on this number line. Use only the denominators 2, 3, 4, 5, 8, and 10. Express numbers greater than 1 as improper fractions.

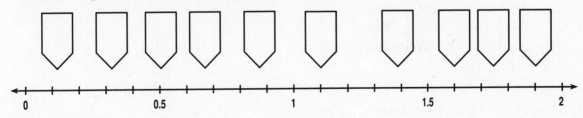

Enrichment Worksheet 6-11

Tagging Along

Which of $\frac{2}{3}$, $\frac{3}{4}$, $\frac{4}{5}$, and $\frac{9}{10}$ belongs in the "tag" on the number line at the right? The tag is to the right of 0.75, so the fraction must be greater than 0.75. Express each fraction as a decimal.

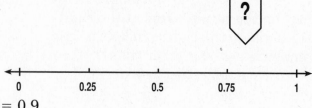

$\frac{2}{3} = 0.\overline{6}$, $\frac{3}{4} = 0.75$, $\frac{4}{5} = 0.8$, $\frac{9}{10} = 0.9$

Only 0.8 and 0.9 are greater than 0.75, and 0.9 is much closer to 1 than to 0.75. Choose 0.8, which is equal to $\frac{4}{5}$.

On each number line, fill in the tags using the given fractions.

1. $\frac{3}{8}, \frac{1}{2}, \frac{2}{3}, \frac{1}{9}, \frac{7}{8}$

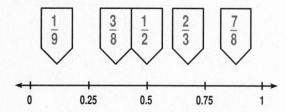

2. $\frac{4}{3}, \frac{3}{4}, \frac{6}{5}, \frac{5}{8}, \frac{15}{16}$

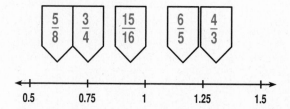

3. $\frac{7}{4}, \frac{6}{5}, \frac{15}{8}, \frac{3}{2}, \frac{4}{3}$

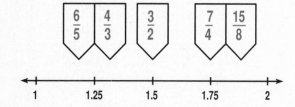

4. $\frac{9}{5}, \frac{7}{3}, \frac{8}{5}, \frac{13}{6}, \frac{8}{4}$

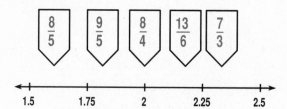

5. Write a fraction in simplest form for each tag on this number line. Use only the denominators 2, 3, 4, 5, 8, and 10. Express numbers greater than 1 as improper fractions.

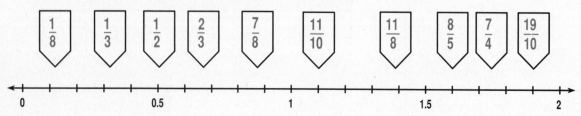

Enrichment Worksheet 7-1

Greatest Possible Error

When you measure a quantity, your measurement is more **precise** when you use a smaller unit of measure. But no measurement is ever exact—there is always some amount of error. The **greatest possible error (GPE)** of a measurement is one half the unit of measure.

At the right, you see how the GPE for the ruler shown is calculated as $\frac{1}{16}$ inch. Since $1\frac{3}{8} = 1\frac{6}{16}$, the actual measure of the line segment may *range* anywhere from $1\frac{5}{16}$ inches to $1\frac{7}{16}$ inches.

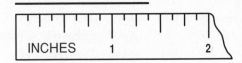

length of line segment:

$1\frac{3}{8}$ inches, to the nearest $\frac{1}{8}$ inch

unit of measure: $\frac{1}{8}$ inch

GPE: half of $\frac{1}{8}$ inch, or $\frac{1}{16}$ inch

Use the GPE to give a range for the measure of each line segment.

1.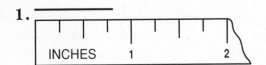

2.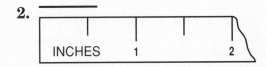

3.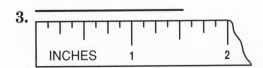

4.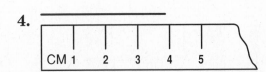

5. Using this scale, the weight of a bag of potatoes is measured as 3 pounds. What is the range for the actual weight of the potatoes?

6. Using this container, the amount of a liquid is measured as 20 milliliters. What is the range for the actual amount of the liquid?

Enrichment Worksheet 7-1

Greatest Possible Error

When you measure a quantity, your measurement is more **precise** when you use a smaller unit of measure. But no measurement is ever exact—there is always some amount of error. The **greatest possible error (GPE)** of a measurement is one half the unit of measure.

At the right, you see how the GPE for the ruler shown is calculated as $\frac{1}{16}$ inch. Since $1\frac{3}{8} = 1\frac{6}{16}$, the actual measure of the line segment may *range* anywhere from $1\frac{5}{16}$ inches to $1\frac{7}{16}$ inches.

length of line segment:

$1\frac{3}{8}$ inches, to the nearest $\frac{1}{8}$ inch

unit of measure: $\frac{1}{8}$ inch

GPE: half of $\frac{1}{8}$ inch, or $\frac{1}{16}$ inch

Use the GPE to give a range for the measure of each line segment.

1.

$\frac{5}{8}$ inch to $\frac{7}{8}$ inch

2.

$\frac{1}{4}$ inch to $\frac{3}{4}$ inch

3.

$1\frac{7}{16}$ inches to $1\frac{9}{16}$ inches

4.

3.5 cm to 4.5 cm

5. Using this scale, the weight of a bag of potatoes is measured as 3 pounds. What is the range for the actual weight of the potatoes?

$2\frac{7}{8}$ pounds to $3\frac{1}{8}$ pounds

6. Using this container, the amount of a liquid is measured as 20 milliliters. What is the range for the actual amount of the liquid?

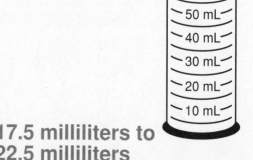

17.5 milliliters to 22.5 milliliters

Glencoe Division, Macmillan/McGraw-Hill

Enrichment Worksheet 7-2

Using One as a Benchmark

When you estimate sums of proper fractions, it often helps to use the number 1 as a *benchmark*, like this.

Two halves make a whole, so $\frac{1}{2} + \frac{1}{2} = 1$.

If two fractions are each less than $\frac{1}{2}$, their sum is less than 1.

$$\frac{3}{8} + \frac{4}{9} < 1$$

If two fractions are each greater than $\frac{1}{2}$, their sum is greater than 1.

$$\frac{5}{8} + \frac{7}{9} > 1$$

Fill in each ☐ **with < or >.**

1. $\frac{2}{3} + \frac{5}{8}$ ☐ 1 2. $\frac{2}{5} + \frac{3}{7}$ ☐ 1 3. $\frac{3}{10} + \frac{5}{11}$ ☐ 1

4. $\frac{27}{50} + \frac{7}{10}$ ☐ 1 5. $\frac{50}{99} + \frac{38}{75}$ ☐ 1 6. $\frac{24}{49} + \frac{32}{65}$ ☐ 1

Fill in each ☐ **with one of the given fractions.**

7. $\frac{2}{7}$ $\frac{3}{7}$ $\frac{4}{7}$ $\frac{5}{7}$ $\frac{1}{2} +$ ☐ > 1 $\frac{1}{2} +$ ☐ < 1

8. $\frac{8}{11}$ $\frac{7}{11}$ $\frac{6}{11}$ $\frac{5}{11}$ $\frac{1}{2} +$ ☐ > 1 $\frac{1}{2} +$ ☐ < 1

9. $\frac{1}{5}$ $\frac{2}{5}$ $\frac{3}{5}$ $\frac{4}{5}$ $\frac{9}{16} +$ ☐ > 1 $\frac{9}{16} +$ ☐ < 1

10. $\frac{1}{25}$ $\frac{12}{25}$ $\frac{13}{25}$ $\frac{24}{25}$ $\frac{6}{13} +$ ☐ > 1 $\frac{6}{13} +$ ☐ < 1

Fill in each ☐ **with < or >.**

11. $1\frac{5}{8} -$ ☐ $\frac{1}{2}$ 12. $1 - \frac{5}{11}$ ☐ $\frac{1}{2}$ 13. $1 - \frac{10}{19}$ ☐ $\frac{1}{2}$

14. $1 - \frac{49}{99}$ ☐ $\frac{1}{2}$ 15. $4\frac{3}{7} + \frac{1}{3}$ ☐ 5 16. $3 - \frac{4}{7}$ ☐ $2\frac{1}{2}$

Enrichment Worksheet 7-2

Using One as a Benchmark

When you estimate sums of proper fractions, it often helps to use the number 1 as a *benchmark*, like this.

Two halves make a whole, so $\frac{1}{2} + \frac{1}{2} = 1$.

If two fractions are each less than $\frac{1}{2}$, their sum is less than 1.

$$\frac{3}{8} + \frac{4}{9} < 1$$

If two fractions are each greater than $\frac{1}{2}$, their sum is greater than 1.

$$\frac{5}{8} + \frac{7}{9} > 1$$

Fill in each ☐ **with < or >.**

1. $\frac{2}{3} + \frac{5}{8}$ $\boxed{>}$ 1

2. $\frac{2}{5} + \frac{3}{7}$ $\boxed{<}$ 1

3. $\frac{3}{10} + \frac{5}{11}$ $\boxed{<}$ 1

4. $\frac{27}{50} + \frac{7}{10}$ $\boxed{>}$ 1

5. $\frac{50}{99} + \frac{38}{75}$ $\boxed{>}$ 1

6. $\frac{24}{49} + \frac{32}{65}$ $\boxed{<}$ 1

**Answers may vary.
A sample answer is given.**

Fill in each ☐ **with one of the given fractions.**

7. $\frac{2}{7}$ $\frac{3}{7}$ $\frac{4}{7}$ $\frac{5}{7}$ $\frac{1}{2} + \boxed{\frac{5}{7}} > 1$ $\frac{1}{2} + \boxed{\frac{2}{7}} < 1$

8. $\frac{8}{11}$ $\frac{7}{11}$ $\frac{6}{11}$ $\frac{5}{11}$ $\frac{1}{2} + \boxed{\frac{6}{11}} > 1$ $\frac{1}{2} + \boxed{\frac{5}{11}} < 1$

9. $\frac{1}{5}$ $\frac{2}{5}$ $\frac{3}{5}$ $\frac{4}{5}$ $\frac{9}{16} + \boxed{\frac{4}{5}} > 1$ $\frac{9}{16} + \boxed{\frac{1}{5}} < 1$

10. $\frac{1}{25}$ $\frac{12}{25}$ $\frac{13}{25}$ $\frac{24}{25}$ $\frac{6}{13} + \boxed{\frac{24}{25}} > 1$ $\frac{6}{13} + \boxed{\frac{1}{25}} < 1$

Fill in each ☐ **with < or >.**

11. $1\frac{5}{8} - \boxed{<} \frac{1}{2}$

12. $1 - \frac{5}{11} \boxed{>} \frac{1}{2}$

13. $1 - \frac{10}{19} \boxed{<} \frac{1}{2}$

14. $1 - \frac{49}{99} \boxed{>} \frac{1}{2}$

15. $4\frac{3}{7} + \frac{1}{3} \boxed{<} 5$

16. $3 - \frac{4}{7} \boxed{<} 2\frac{1}{2}$

Enrichment Worksheet 7-3

Mystic Hexagons

A **hexagon** is a six-sided figure. In a *mystic hexagon*, the sum of the numbers along each side is the same number. This number is called the *mystic sum*. For example, the mystic sum for the hexagon at the right is 20.

For each mystic hexagon, write the mystic sum in the blank in the middle. Then find the missing fractions along the sides.

1.

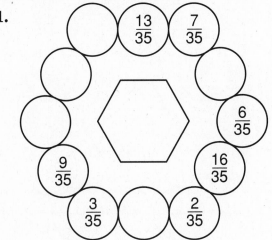

2.

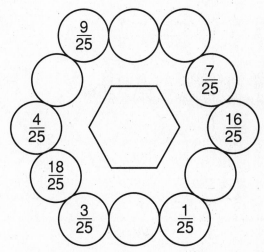

First complete each mystic hexagon. Then be sure to express all your answers in simplest form.

3.

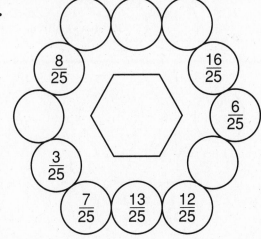

4.

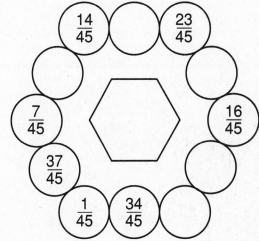

Enrichment Worksheet 7-3

Mystic Hexagons

A **hexagon** is a six-sided figure. In a *mystic hexagon*, the sum of the numbers along each side is the same number. This number is called the *mystic sum*. For example, the mystic sum for the hexagon at the right is 20.

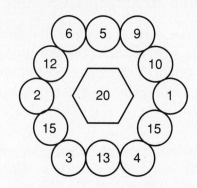

For each mystic hexagon, write the mystic sum in the blank in the middle. Then find the missing fractions along the sides.

1.

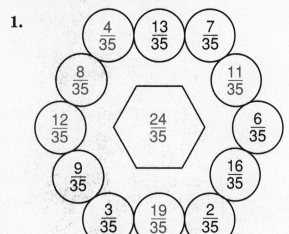

2.

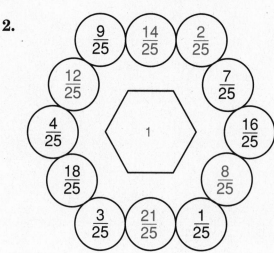

First complete each mystic hexagon. Then be sure to express all your answers in simplest form.

3.

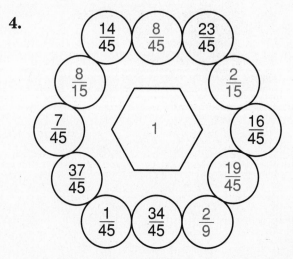

4.

Enrichment Worksheet 7-4

Equations with Fractions and Decimals

Sometimes an equation involves both fractions and decimals. To solve an equation like this, you probably want to work with numbers in the same form. One method of doing this is to start by expressing the decimals as fractions. The example at the right shows how you might solve the equation $m + \frac{1}{3} = 0.\overline{6}$.

$$m + \frac{1}{3} = 0.\overline{6}$$

$$m + \frac{1}{3} = \frac{2}{3} \longleftarrow \text{Write } 0.\overline{6} \text{ as a fraction.}$$

$$m = \frac{2}{3} - \frac{1}{3}$$

$$m = \frac{1}{3}$$

Name the number that is a solution of the given equation.

1. $z = \frac{1}{8} + 0.375;$ $\quad \frac{1}{8}, \frac{3}{8}, \frac{1}{2}, \frac{3}{4}$

2. $0.75 - \frac{3}{4} = b;$ $\quad 0, \frac{1}{4}, 1, 1\frac{1}{4}$

3. $c + 0.6 = \frac{4}{5};$ $\quad \frac{1}{5}, \frac{3}{5}, 1\frac{1}{5}, 1\frac{2}{5}$

4. $0.\overline{6} = j - \frac{1}{3};$ $\quad \frac{1}{3}, \frac{2}{3}, 1, 1\frac{1}{3}$

5. $\frac{1}{4} + r = 0.75;$ $\quad \frac{1}{4}, \frac{1}{2}, \frac{3}{4}, 1$

6. $d - 0.1 = \frac{7}{10};$ $\quad \frac{1}{2}, \frac{3}{5}, \frac{4}{5}, \frac{9}{10},$

Solve each equation. If the solution is a fraction or a mixed number, be sure to express it in simplest form.

7. $\frac{2}{5} + 0.4 = k$

8. $s = \frac{7}{8} - 0.125$

9. $0.\overline{6} = n - \frac{2}{3}$

10. $t + 0.2 = \frac{4}{5}$

11. $0.375 + g = \frac{5}{8}$

12. $y - 0.25 = \frac{3}{4}$

13. $0.8 - \frac{1}{5} = x$

14. $q + 0.125 = \frac{5}{8}$

15. $w = \frac{1}{8} + 0.375 + \frac{5}{8}$

16. $0.7 + \frac{1}{10} - 0.3 = a$

17. $p + \frac{1}{5} = 0.8 - \frac{3}{5}$

18. $k - 0.875 = 0.375 + \frac{1}{8}$

60

Enrichment Worksheet 7-4

Equations with Fractions and Decimals

Sometimes an equation involves both fractions and decimals. To solve an equation like this, you probably want to work with numbers in the same form. One method of doing this is to start by expressing the decimals as fractions. The example at the right shows how you might solve the equation $m + \frac{1}{3} = 0.\overline{6}$.

$$m + \frac{1}{3} = 0.\overline{6}$$

$$m + \frac{1}{3} = \frac{2}{3} \longleftarrow \text{Write } 0.\overline{6} \text{ as a fraction.}$$

$$m = \frac{2}{3} - \frac{1}{3}$$

$$m = \frac{1}{3}$$

Name the number that is a solution of the given equation.

1. $z = \frac{1}{8} + 0.375$; $\frac{1}{8}, \frac{3}{8}, \frac{1}{2}, \frac{3}{4}$ **$\frac{1}{2}$**

2. $0.75 - \frac{3}{4} = b$; $0, \frac{1}{4}, 1, 1\frac{1}{4}$ **0**

3. $c + 0.6 = \frac{4}{5}$; $\frac{1}{5}, \frac{3}{5}, 1\frac{1}{5}, 1\frac{2}{5}$ **$\frac{1}{5}$**

4. $0.\overline{6} = j - \frac{1}{3}$; $\frac{1}{3}, \frac{2}{3}, 1, 1\frac{1}{3}$ **1**

5. $\frac{1}{4} + r = 0.75$; $\frac{1}{4}, \frac{1}{2}, \frac{3}{4}, 1$ **$\frac{1}{2}$**

6. $d - 0.1 = \frac{7}{10}$; $\frac{1}{2}, \frac{3}{5}, \frac{4}{5}, \frac{9}{10},$ **$\frac{4}{5}$**

Solve each equation. If the solution is a fraction or a mixed number, be sure to express it in simplest form.

7. $\frac{2}{5} + 0.4 = k$ **$\frac{4}{5}$**

8. $s = \frac{7}{8} - 0.125$ **$\frac{3}{4}$**

9. $0.\overline{6} = n - \frac{2}{3}$ **$1\frac{1}{3}$**

10. $t + 0.2 = \frac{4}{5}$ **$\frac{3}{5}$**

11. $0.375 + g = \frac{5}{8}$ **$\frac{1}{4}$**

12. $y - 0.25 = \frac{3}{4}$ **1**

13. $0.8 - \frac{1}{5} = x$ **$\frac{3}{5}$**

14. $q + 0.125 = \frac{5}{8}$ **$\frac{1}{2}$**

15. $w = \frac{1}{8} + 0.375 + \frac{5}{8}$ **$1\frac{1}{8}$**

16. $0.7 + \frac{1}{10} - 0.3 = a$ **$\frac{1}{2}$**

17. $p + \frac{1}{5} = 0.8 - \frac{3}{5}$ **0**

18. $k - 0.875 = 0.375 + \frac{1}{8}$ **$1\frac{3}{8}$**

Name ______________________________ Date ______________

Enrichment Worksheet 7-5

Unit Fractions

A **unit fraction** is a fraction whose numerator is 1 and whose denominator is any counting number greater than 1.

unit fractions → $\frac{1}{2}$ $\frac{1}{3}$ $\frac{1}{10}$

A curious fact about unit fractions is that each one can be expressed as a sum of two distinct unit fractions. (*Distinct* means that the two new fractions are different from one another.)

$\frac{1}{2} = \frac{1}{3} + \frac{1}{6}$ $\frac{1}{3} = \frac{1}{4} + \frac{1}{12}$ $\frac{1}{10} = \frac{1}{11} + \frac{1}{110}$

Did you know?

The *Rhind Papyrus* indicates that fractions were used in ancient Egypt nearly 4,000 years ago. If a fraction was not a unit fraction, the Egyptians wrote it as a sum of unit fractions. The only exception to this rule seems to be the fraction $\frac{2}{3}$.

1. The three sums shown above follow a pattern. What is it?

2. Use the pattern you described in Exercise 1. Express each unit fraction as a sum of two distinct unit fractions.

a. $\frac{1}{4}$ **b.** $\frac{1}{5}$ **c.** $\frac{1}{12}$ **d.** $\frac{1}{100}$

Does it surprise you to know that other fractions, such as $\frac{5}{6}$, can be expressed as sums of unit fractions? One way to do this is by using equivalent fractions. Here's how.

$\frac{5}{6} = \frac{10}{12} \rightarrow \frac{10}{12} = \frac{6}{12} + \frac{4}{12} = \frac{1}{2} + \frac{1}{3} \rightarrow \frac{5}{6} = \frac{1}{2} + \frac{1}{3}$

3. Express each fraction as a sum of two distinct unit fractions.

a. $\frac{2}{3}$ **b.** $\frac{4}{15}$ **c.** $\frac{5}{9}$ **d.** $\frac{2}{5}$

4. Express $\frac{4}{5}$ as the sum of *three* distinct unit fractions.

5. ***CHALLENGE*** Show two different ways to express $\frac{1}{2}$ as the sum of three distinct unit fractions.

Glencoe Division, Macmillan/McGraw-Hill

Enrichment Worksheet 7-5

Unit Fractions

A **unit fraction** is a fraction whose numerator is 1 and whose denominator is any counting number greater than 1.

$$\text{unit fractions} \longrightarrow \frac{1}{2} \quad \frac{1}{3} \quad \frac{1}{10}$$

A curious fact about unit fractions is that each one can be expressed as a sum of two distinct unit fractions. (*Distinct* means that the two new fractions are different from one another.)

$$\frac{1}{2} = \frac{1}{3} + \frac{1}{6} \qquad \frac{1}{3} = \frac{1}{4} + \frac{1}{12} \qquad \frac{1}{10} = \frac{1}{11} + \frac{1}{110}$$

> **Did you know?**
> The *Rhind Papyrus* indicates that fractions were used in ancient Egypt nearly 4,000 years ago. If a fraction was not a unit fraction, the Egyptians wrote it as a sum of unit fractions. The only exception to this rule seems to be the fraction $\frac{2}{3}$.

1. The three sums shown above follow a pattern. What is it?
   Let n be the denominator of the given fraction. The denominators of the distinct unit fractions are $(n + 1)$ and $n(n + 1)$.

2. Use the pattern you described in Exercise 1. Express each unit fraction as a sum of two distinct unit fractions.

   a. $\frac{1}{4}$ $\quad \frac{1}{5} + \frac{1}{20}$ **b.** $\frac{1}{5}$ $\quad \frac{1}{6} + \frac{1}{30}$ **c.** $\frac{1}{12}$ $\quad \frac{1}{13} + \frac{1}{156}$ **d.** $\frac{1}{100}$ $\quad \frac{1}{101} + \frac{1}{10{,}100}$

Does it surprise you to know that other fractions, such as $\frac{5}{6}$, can be expressed as sums of unit fractions? One way to do this is by using equivalent fractions. Here's how.

$$\frac{5}{6} = \frac{10}{12} \quad \rightarrow \quad \frac{10}{12} = \frac{6}{12} + \frac{4}{12} = \frac{1}{2} + \frac{1}{3} \quad \rightarrow \quad \frac{5}{6} = \frac{1}{2} + \frac{1}{3}$$

3. Express each fraction as a sum of two distinct unit fractions.

   a. $\frac{2}{3}$ $\quad \frac{1}{2} + \frac{1}{6}$ **b.** $\frac{4}{15}$ $\quad \frac{1}{5} + \frac{1}{15}$ **c.** $\frac{5}{9}$ $\quad \frac{1}{2} + \frac{1}{18}$ **d.** $\frac{2}{5}$ $\quad \frac{1}{3} + \frac{1}{15}$

4. Express $\frac{4}{5}$ as the sum of *three* distinct unit fractions. $\quad \frac{1}{2} + \frac{1}{4} + \frac{1}{20}$

5. **CHALLENGE** Show two different ways to express $\frac{1}{2}$ as the sum of three distinct unit fractions.
   $\frac{1}{4} + \frac{1}{6} + \frac{1}{12}; \frac{1}{3} + \frac{1}{7} + \frac{1}{42}$

Enrichment Worksheet 7-6

Tangrams

The **tangram** is an ancient Chinese puzzle. It is made up of the seven puzzle pieces that you see at the right. To do the activities on this page, trace the tangram onto a separate piece of paper, then cut out the squares.

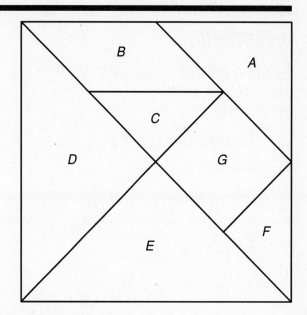

1. Suppose that the area of the entire tangram is 1 square unit. What is the area of each piece?

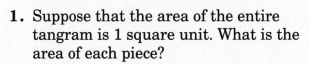

2. Now suppose that the area of the small square labeled **G** is 1 square unit. What is the area of the entire tangram?

3. Assume that the area of the triangle labeled **D** is 1 square unit. Find the area of each figure. (*Hint:* First decide which of the puzzle pieces join together to form the figure.

a.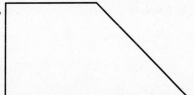

b.

c.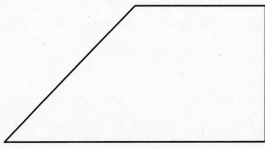

d.

4. **CHALLENGE** Show how to arrange all seven pieces to form a rectangle whose length is twice its width.

Enrichment Worksheet 7-6

Tangrams

The **tangram** is an ancient Chinese puzzle. It is made up of the seven puzzle pieces that you see at the right. To do the activities on this page, trace the tangram onto a separate piece of paper, then cut out the squares.

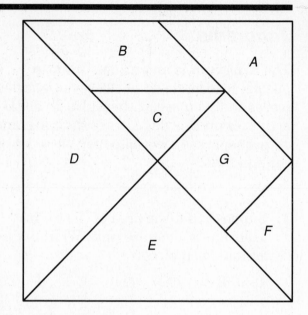

1. Suppose that the area of the entire tangram is 1 square unit. What is the area of each piece?

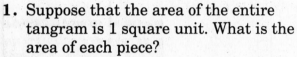

A	*B*	*C*	*D*	*E*	*F*	*G*
$\frac{1}{8}$	$\frac{1}{8}$	$\frac{1}{16}$	$\frac{1}{4}$	$\frac{1}{4}$	$\frac{1}{16}$	$\frac{1}{8}$

2. Now suppose that the area of the small square labeled *G* is 1 square unit. What is the area of the entire tangram?

   8 square units

3. Assume that the area of the triangle labeled *D* is 1 square unit. Find the area of each figure. (*Hint:* First decide which of the puzzle pieces join together to form the figure.)

   a. 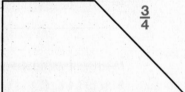 $\frac{3}{4}$

   b. 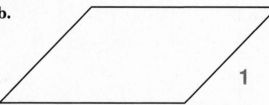 1

   c. $1\frac{1}{2}$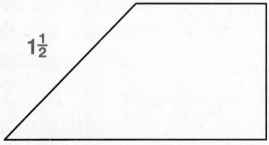

   d. 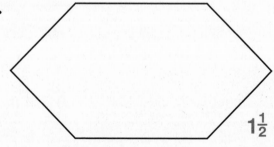 $1\frac{1}{2}$

4. **CHALLENGE** Show how to arrange all seven pieces to form a rectangle whose length is twice its width.

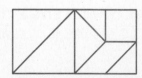

Enrichment Worksheet 7-7

The Stock Market

When you buy **stock** in a company, you become a part owner in that company. You buy stock in units called **shares**. The stock report that you see in a newspaper lists high and low prices per share of stock. The prices are given as whole dollars or as halves, fourths, or eighths of a dollar.

Find the difference between the high and low prices for each stock listed. The difference for Avon is shown as an example.

	High	Low	Stock	Difference
	49⅜	32¼	Avon	49 3/8 − 32 1/4 = 17 1/8
1.	23 ¾	12 ⅝	Caldor	
2.	44 ⅜	26 ¾	Gn Motr	
3.	45 ¼	36 ½	Hrshey	
4.	51 ¼	29 ⅜	K mart	
5.	67	38 ¼	Kellogg's	
6.	45	26 ⅜	McDonl	
7.	75 ¾	46 ⅞	QuakrO	
8.	43 ½	25 ⅛	Sears	
9.	39 ⅜	28	Walgrn	
10.	78	43 ⅛	Xerox	

11. What stock listed above had the greatest difference between high and low prices? the least difference?

12. What would be the price of a share of Quaker Oats stock if it rose 2 ½ above its high?

Glencoe Division, Macmillan/McGraw-Hill

Name ______________________ Date ______________

Enrichment Worksheet 7-7

The Stock Market

When you buy **stock** in a company, you become a part owner in that company. You buy stock in units called **shares**. The stock report that you see in a newspaper lists high and low prices per share of stock. The prices are given as whole dollars or as halves, fourths, or eighths of a dollar.

Find the difference between the high and low prices for each stock listed. The difference for Avon is shown as an example.

	High	Low	Stock	Difference
	49⅜	32¼	Avon	49 3/8 − 32 1/4 = 17 1/8
1.	23 ¾	12 ⅝	Caldor	11 ⅛
2.	44 ⅜	26 ¾	Gn Motr	17 ⅝
3.	45 ¼	36 ½	Hrshey	8 ¾
4.	51 ¼	29 ⅜	K mart	21 ⅞
5.	67	38 ¼	Kellogg's	28 ¾
6.	45	26 ⅜	McDonl	18 ⅝
7.	75 ¾	46 ⅞	QuakrO	28 ⅞
8.	43 ½	25 ⅛	Sears	18 ⅜
9.	39 ⅜	28	Walgrn	11 ⅜
10.	78	43 ⅛	Xerox	34 ⅞

11. What stock listed above had the greatest difference between high and low prices? the least difference?
Xerox; Hrshey

12. What would be the price of a share of Quaker Oats stock if it rose 2 ½ above its high? **78 ¼**

Glencoe Division, Macmillan/McGraw-Hill

Enrichment Worksheet 7-8

Fractions of Time

Denise organized information about some of her activities into the chart you see at the right. Then she decided to estimate what fraction of the school day she spends studying. This is how she did it.

4:00 P.M.–5:15 P.M. → 1 h 15 min

7:00 P.M.–8:00 P.M. → <u>1 h</u>

Total   2 h 15 min

Then she rounded 2 h 15 min to 2 h.

breakfast	7:15 A.M. - 7:30 A.M.
classes	8:05 A.M. - 11:30 A.M.
lunch	11:30 A.M. - 12:20 P.M.
classes	12:20 P.M. - 2:15 P.M.
swimming	2:25 P.M. - 3:30 P.M.
studying	4:00 P.M. - 5:15 P.M.
dinner	5:30 P.M. - 6:30 P.M.
studying	7:00 P.M. - 8:00 P.M.
watching TV	8:00 P.M. - 9:55 P.M.
sleeping	10:30 P.M. - 6:45 A.M.

Denise estimated that she spends about $\frac{2}{24}$, or $\frac{1}{12}$, of her day studying.

Use the chart above. Estimate what fraction of a school day Denise spends on each activity.

1. swimming

2. watching TV

3. classes

4. eating

5. sleeping

6. at school (classes and lunch)

7. Denise sleeps from 11:30 P.M. until 8:30 A.M. on Saturday and Sunday. About what fraction of the seven-day week does she spend sleeping?

8. Denise studies about 4 hours on Saturday and about 2 hours on Sunday. About what fraction of the seven-day week does she spend studying?

9. Denise goes to school 180 days of the year. About what fraction of the 365-day year does she spend in classes?

10. Denise tries to swim every day at the same time, Monday through Friday, all through the year. About what fraction of the year does she spend swimming?

Enrichment Worksheet 7-8

Fractions of Time

Denise organized information about some of her activities into the chart you see at the right. Then she decided to estimate what fraction of the school day she spends studying. This is how she did it.

breakfast	7:15 A.M. - 7:30 A.M.
classes	8:05 A.M. - 11:30 A.M.
lunch	11:30 A.M. - 12:20 P.M.
classes	12:20 P.M. - 2:15 P.M.
swimming	2:25 P.M. - 3:30 P.M.
studying	4:00 P.M. - 5:15 P.M.
dinner	5:30 P.M. - 6:30 P.M.
studying	7:00 P.M. - 8:00 P.M.
watching TV	8:00 P.M. - 9:55 P.M.
sleeping	10:30 P.M. - 6:45 A.M.

4:00 P.M.–5:15 P.M. $\rightarrow$ 1 h 15 min

7:00 P.M.–8:00 P.M. $\rightarrow$ <u>1 h</u>

        Total   2 h 15 min

Then she rounded 2 h 15 min to 2 h.

Denise estimated that she spends about $\frac{2}{24}$, or $\frac{1}{12}$, of her day studying.

Use the chart above. Estimate what fraction of a school day Denise spends on each activity.

Estimates may vary.

1. swimming **about** $\frac{1}{24}$

2. watching TV **about** $\frac{1}{12}$

3. classes **about** $\frac{5}{24}$

4. eating **about** $\frac{1}{12}$

5. sleeping **about** $\frac{1}{3}$

6. at school (classes and lunch)
   about $\frac{1}{4}$

7. Denise sleeps from 11:30 P.M. until 8:30 A.M. on Saturday and Sunday. About what fraction of the seven-day week does she spend sleeping?
   about $\frac{3}{8}$

8. Denise studies about 4 hours on Saturday and about 2 hours on Sunday. About what fraction of the seven-day week does she spend studying? **about** $\frac{1}{10}$

9. Denise goes to school 180 days of the year. About what fraction of the 365-day year does she spend in classes? **about** $\frac{1}{10}$

10. Denise tries to swim every day at the same time, Monday through Friday, all through the year. About what fraction of the year does she spend swimming? **about** $\frac{1}{30}$

Enrichment Worksheet 7-9

Trail Blazers

Each puzzle on this page is called a **trail blazer**. To solve it, you must find a trail that begins at any one of the small squares and ends at the goal square, following these rules.

1. The sum of all the fractions on the trail must equal the number in the goal square.
2. The trail can only go horizontally or vertically.
3. The trail cannot retrace or cross itself.

When you are solving a trail blazer, try to eliminate possibilities. For instance, in the puzzle at the right, you know that you cannot include $\frac{3}{4}$: $\frac{3}{4} + \frac{1}{4} = 1$ and $\frac{3}{4} + \frac{1}{2} = 1\frac{1}{4}$, while the goal for the entire trail is only 1.

$\frac{3}{4}$	$\frac{1}{2}$	$\frac{1}{4}$
$\frac{1}{4}$	$\frac{3}{16}$	$\frac{1}{8}$
$\frac{1}{8}$	$\frac{1}{16}$	$\frac{5}{8}$

1 ← goal square

1.

$\frac{1}{12}$	$\frac{2}{3}$	$\frac{5}{6}$
$\frac{1}{2}$	$\frac{5}{12}$	$\frac{1}{6}$
$\frac{7}{12}$	$\frac{1}{3}$	$\frac{1}{12}$

1

2.

$\frac{4}{5}$	$\frac{1}{5}$	$\frac{3}{5}$
$\frac{7}{10}$	$\frac{1}{2}$	$\frac{2}{5}$
$\frac{9}{10}$	$\frac{3}{10}$	$\frac{1}{10}$

$2\frac{1}{2}$

3.

$\frac{7}{8}$	$\frac{2}{3}$	$\frac{3}{8}$
$\frac{5}{12}$	$\frac{3}{4}$	$\frac{5}{8}$
$\frac{1}{2}$	$\frac{1}{4}$	$\frac{1}{3}$

$3\frac{1}{2}$

4.

$\frac{3}{8}$	$\frac{3}{4}$	$\frac{1}{8}$	$\frac{3}{8}$	$\frac{1}{2}$
$\frac{1}{8}$	$\frac{7}{8}$	$\frac{1}{4}$	$\frac{7}{8}$	$\frac{1}{4}$
$\frac{1}{2}$	$\frac{3}{8}$	$\frac{5}{8}$	$\frac{1}{8}$	$\frac{1}{2}$
$\frac{7}{8}$	$\frac{1}{8}$	$\frac{1}{4}$	$\frac{1}{2}$	$\frac{1}{8}$
$\frac{1}{4}$	$\frac{3}{4}$	$\frac{1}{2}$	$\frac{1}{4}$	$\frac{3}{4}$

6

5.

$\frac{1}{20}$	$\frac{17}{20}$	$\frac{1}{4}$	$\frac{2}{5}$	$\frac{1}{10}$
$\frac{4}{5}$	$\frac{1}{2}$	$\frac{11}{20}$	$\frac{3}{20}$	$\frac{1}{5}$
$\frac{7}{10}$	$\frac{1}{20}$	$\frac{3}{4}$	$\frac{1}{4}$	$\frac{19}{20}$
$\frac{1}{5}$	$\frac{13}{20}$	$\frac{3}{10}$	$\frac{3}{5}$	$\frac{1}{2}$
$\frac{9}{20}$	$\frac{1}{10}$	$\frac{1}{5}$	$\frac{7}{20}$	$\frac{1}{4}$

4

Enrichment Worksheet 7-9

Trail Blazers

Each puzzle on this page is called a **trail blazer**. To solve it, you must find a trail that begins at any one of the small squares and ends at the goal square, following these rules.

1. The sum of all the fractions on the trail must equal the number in the goal square.
2. The trail can only go horizontally or vertically.
3. The trail cannot retrace or cross itself.

When you are solving a trail blazer, try to eliminate possibilities. For instance, in the puzzle at the right, you know that you cannot include $\frac{3}{4}$: $\frac{3}{4} + \frac{1}{4} = 1$ and $\frac{3}{4} + \frac{1}{2} = 1\frac{1}{4}$, while the goal for the entire trail is only 1.   **Answers may vary.**

$\frac{3}{4}$	$\frac{1}{2}$	$\frac{1}{4}$
$\frac{1}{4}$	$\frac{3}{16}$	$\frac{1}{8}$
$\frac{1}{8}$	$\frac{1}{16}$	$\frac{5}{8}$

1 ← goal square

1.

$\frac{1}{12}$	$\frac{2}{3}$	$\frac{5}{6}$
$\frac{1}{2}$	$\frac{5}{12}$	$\frac{1}{6}$
$\frac{7}{12}$	$\frac{1}{3}$	$\frac{1}{12}$

1

2.

$\frac{4}{5}$	$\frac{1}{5}$	$\frac{3}{5}$
$\frac{7}{10}$	$\frac{1}{2}$	$\frac{2}{5}$
$\frac{9}{10}$	$\frac{3}{10}$	$\frac{1}{10}$

$2\frac{1}{2}$

3.

$\frac{7}{8}$	$\frac{2}{3}$	$\frac{3}{8}$
$\frac{5}{12}$	$\frac{3}{4}$	$\frac{5}{8}$
$\frac{1}{2}$	$\frac{1}{4}$	$\frac{1}{3}$

$3\frac{1}{2}$

4.

$\frac{3}{8}$	$\frac{3}{4}$	$\frac{1}{8}$	$\frac{3}{8}$	$\frac{1}{2}$
$\frac{1}{8}$	$\frac{7}{8}$	$\frac{1}{4}$	$\frac{7}{8}$	$\frac{1}{4}$
$\frac{1}{2}$	$\frac{3}{8}$	$\frac{5}{8}$	$\frac{1}{8}$	$\frac{1}{2}$
$\frac{7}{8}$	$\frac{1}{8}$	$\frac{1}{4}$	$\frac{1}{2}$	$\frac{1}{8}$
$\frac{1}{4}$	$\frac{3}{4}$	$\frac{1}{2}$	$\frac{1}{4}$	$\frac{3}{4}$

6

5.

$\frac{1}{20}$	$\frac{17}{20}$	$\frac{1}{4}$	$\frac{2}{5}$	$\frac{1}{10}$
$\frac{4}{5}$	$\frac{1}{2}$	$\frac{11}{20}$	$\frac{3}{20}$	$\frac{1}{5}$
$\frac{7}{10}$	$\frac{1}{20}$	$\frac{3}{4}$	$\frac{1}{4}$	$\frac{19}{20}$
$\frac{1}{5}$	$\frac{13}{20}$	$\frac{3}{10}$	$\frac{3}{5}$	$\frac{1}{2}$
$\frac{9}{20}$	$\frac{1}{10}$	$\frac{1}{5}$	$\frac{7}{20}$	$\frac{1}{4}$

4

Glencoe Division, Macmillan/McGraw-Hill

Enrichment Worksheet 8-1

Shopping with Compatible Numbers

Suppose that you are meeting a friend for lunch and come across the sale advertised at the right. For weeks, you have wanted to buy a set of CDs that is regularly priced at $31.98. Here is how compatible numbers can help you find the sale price of the set.

- $\frac{1}{4}$ of $31.98 is about $\frac{1}{4}$ of $32, or $8.

- "$\frac{1}{4}$ off" means that you pay $1 - \frac{1}{4}$, or $\frac{3}{4}$.

- Since $\frac{1}{4}$ of $32 = $8, $\frac{3}{4}$ of $32 = $24.

The sale price is about $24.

Each exercise gives the regular price of one or more items. Use the information at the right to estimate the sale price.

Savings Riot

One-Day Discounts

1/4 Off Every CD in Stock

1/3 Off Every CASSETTE in Stock

1/2 Off
- ALL HEADPHONES
- TRUE-CELL BATTERIES

$2.00 OFF ALL VIDEOS

1. cassette: $8.95

2. CD: $14.95

3. headphones: $10.98

4. three packs of TRUE-CELL batteries; $5.98 per pack

5. one CD: $20.95
   one cassette: $11.95

6. one set of headphones: $15.79
   two cassettes: $4.98 and $6.98

7. one CD: $16.95
   one set of headphones: $14.50
   one video: $19.98

8. two CDs: $14.95 and $12.95
   one cassette: $7.98
   two videos: $14.95 each

Enrichment Worksheet 8-1

Shopping with Compatible Numbers

Suppose that you are meeting a friend for lunch and come across the sale advertised at the right. For weeks, you have wanted to buy a set of CDs that is regularly priced at $31.98. Here is how compatible numbers can help you find the sale price of the set.

- $\frac{1}{4}$ of $31.98 is about $\frac{1}{4}$ of $32, or $8.

- "$\frac{1}{4}$ off" means that you pay $1 - \frac{1}{4}$, or $\frac{3}{4}$.

- Since $\frac{1}{4}$ of $32 = $8, $\frac{3}{4}$ of $32 = $24.

The sale price is about $24.

Each exercise gives the regular price of one or more items. Use the information at the right to estimate the sale price.

Savings Riot

One-Day Discounts

1/4 Off Every CD in Stock

1/3 Off Every CASSETTE in Stock

1/2 Off
- ALL HEADPHONES
- TRUE-CELL BATTERIES

$2.00 OFF ALL VIDEOS

Estimates may vary.

1. cassette: $8.95   **about $6**

2. CD: $14.95   **about $12**

3. headphones: $10.98   **about $5.50**

4. three packs of TRUE-CELL batteries; $5.98 per pack   **about $9**

5. one CD: $20.95
   one cassette: $11.95
   about $23

6. one set of headphones: $15.79
   two cassettes: $4.98 and $6.98
   about $16

7. one CD: $16.95
   one set of headphones: $14.50
   one video: $19.98
   about $37

8. two CDs: $14.95 and $12.95
   one cassette: $7.98
   two videos: $14.95 each
   about $53

Glencoe Division, Macmillan/McGraw-Hill

Enrichment Worksheet 8-2

Word Sums

Can one sixth plus one third equal one? It is possible if the fractions are fractions of *words*! Here is an example.

Find the last one sixth of the word TOMATO: O
Find the middle one third of the word FINEST: NE
Add the letters O + NE = ONE!

Match each word sum in the first column with its definition in the second column.

1. the first one fourth of CHECKERS
   + the last one half of AFFAIR

2. the first one half of CLOSET
   + the last one fourth of DOWNTOWN

3. the first one fifth of BACKGROUND
   + the middle one third of WONDER

4. the middle one third of ADVENTURE
   + the last one third of LEADER

5. the middle one third of BUGLER
   + the last one fourth of SATISFACTORY

6. the first two thirds of TICKET
   + the last four fifths of STOCK

7. the middle one half of SEAT
   + the last one half of FOURTH

8. the first two fifths of BOARD
   + the middle one half of DAUGHTER

9. the first one half of MARBLE
   + the last three fifths of SUGAR
   + the last one fourth of CLARINET

10. the last two thirds of EAT
    + the first one third of LANDSLIDE
    + the first one fifth of TABLESPOON

a. purchased

b. clock sound

c. capital of Georgia

d. to come into a room

e. where we live

f. honor

g. circus act

h. place to sit

i. woman's name

j. music makers

Enrichment Worksheet 8-2

Word Sums

Can one sixth plus one third equal one? It is possible if the fractions are fractions of *words*! Here is an example.

Find the last one sixth of the word TOMATO: O
Find the middle one third of the word FINEST: NE
Add the letters O + NE = ONE!

Match each word sum in the first column with its definition in the second column.

1. the first one fourth of CHECKERS
   + the last one half of AFFAIR   **h**   **a.** purchased

2. the first one half of CLOSET
   + the last one fourth of DOWNTOWN   **g**   **b.** clock sound

3. the first one fifth of BACKGROUND
   + the middle one third of WONDER   **j**   **c.** capital of Georgia

4. the middle one third of ADVENTURE
   + the last one third of LEADER   **d**   **d.** to come into a room

5. the middle one third of BUGLER
   + the last one fourth of SATISFACTORY **f**   **e.** where we live

6. the first two thirds of TICKET
   + the last four fifths of STOCK   **b**   **f.** honor

7. the middle one half of SEAT
   + the last one half of FOURTH   **e**   **g.** circus act

8. the first two fifths of BOARD
   + the middle one half of DAUGHTER   **a**   **h.** place to sit

9. the first one half of MARBLE
   + the last three fifths of SUGAR
   + the last one fourth of CLARINET   **i**   **i.** woman's name

10. the last two thirds of EAT
    + the first one third of LANDSLIDE
    + the first one fifth of TABLESPOON   **c**   **j.** music makers

Enrichment Worksheet 8-3

Mixed Numbers and Mental Math

Sometimes you can multiply a whole number and a mixed number in your head. The trick is to think of the mixed number in two parts – the whole number and the fraction.

Find each product mentally.

Example   Think: 3×10 Think: $\frac{1}{2}$ of 10

$3\frac{1}{2} \times 10 =$ ___30___ + ___5___ = ___35___

1. $7\frac{1}{2} \times 6 =$ _____ + _____ = _____

2. $4 \times 9\frac{1}{2} =$ _____ + _____ = _____

3. $4\frac{1}{3} \times 6 =$ _____ + _____ = _____

4. $5\frac{1}{4} \times 8 =$ _____ + _____ = _____

5. $15 \times 2\frac{1}{5} =$ _____ + _____ = _____

6. $12 \times 4\frac{1}{6} =$ _____ + _____ = _____

7. $1\frac{2}{3} \times 6 =$ _____ + _____ = _____

8. $5\frac{3}{4} \times 20 =$ _____ + _____ = _____

Now you can use this mental math technique to make better estimates. Here's how.

Estimate the product: $4\frac{1}{2} \times 11\frac{7}{9}$

$4\frac{1}{2} \times 11\frac{7}{9} \rightarrow 4\frac{1}{2} \times 12$

$4\frac{1}{2} \times 12 = 4 \times 12 + \frac{1}{2}$ of 12

$\qquad = 48 + 6$

$\qquad = 54$

So, $4\frac{1}{2} \times 11\frac{7}{9}$ is about 54.

Estimate by rounding only one factor.

9. $6\frac{1}{2} \times 4\frac{2}{11}$

10. $5\frac{1}{3} \times 8\frac{9}{10}$

11. $11\frac{15}{16} \times 2\frac{1}{4}$

12. $5\frac{7}{10} \times 4\frac{1}{6}$

13. $1\frac{2}{3} \times 14\frac{6}{7}$

14. $19\frac{2}{7} \times 1\frac{3}{4}$

Enrichment Worksheet 8-3

Mixed Numbers and Mental Math

Sometimes you can multiply a whole number and a
mixed number in your head. The trick is to think of
the mixed number in two parts – the whole number
and the fraction.

Find each product mentally.

Example   Think: 3×10 Think: $\frac{1}{2}$ of 10

$3\frac{1}{2} \times 10 =$ _____30_____ + _____5_____ = _____35_____

1. $7\frac{1}{2} \times 6 =$ _____42_____ + _____3_____ = _____45_____

2. $4 \times 9\frac{1}{2} =$ _____36_____ + _____2_____ = _____38_____

3. $4\frac{1}{3} \times 6 =$ _____24_____ + _____2_____ = _____26_____

4. $5\frac{1}{4} \times 8 =$ _____40_____ + _____2_____ = _____42_____

5. $15 \times 2\frac{1}{5} =$ _____30_____ + _____3_____ = _____33_____

6. $12 \times 4\frac{1}{6} =$ _____48_____ + _____2_____ = _____50_____

7. $1\frac{2}{3} \times 6 =$ _____6_____ + _____4_____ = _____10_____

8. $5\frac{3}{4} \times 20 =$ _____100_____ + _____15_____ = _____115_____

Now you can use this mental math
technique to make better estimates.
Here's how.

Estimate the product: $4\frac{1}{2} \times 11\frac{7}{9}$

$4\frac{1}{2} \times 11\frac{7}{9} \rightarrow 4\frac{1}{2} \times 12$

$4\frac{1}{2} \times 12 = 4 \times 12 + \frac{1}{2}$ of 12

       $= 48 + 6$

       $= 54$

So, $4\frac{1}{2} \times 11\frac{7}{9}$ is about 54.

Estimate by rounding only one factor.

9. $6\frac{1}{2} \times 4\frac{2}{11}$ **about 26**

10. $5\frac{1}{3} \times 8\frac{9}{10}$ **about 48**

11. $11\frac{15}{16} \times 2\frac{1}{4}$ **about 27**

12. $5\frac{7}{10} \times 4\frac{1}{6}$ **about 25**

13. $1\frac{2}{3} \times 14\frac{6}{7}$ **about 25**

14. $19\frac{2}{7} \times 1\frac{3}{4}$ **about 35**

Glencoe Division, Macmillan/McGraw-Hill

Enrichment Worksheet 8-4

Extending Problems

When examining the solution of a problem, good problem solvers look for ways to extend the problem. The questions on this page show you a way to examine and extend the following pattern.

Row 1: $\frac{1}{2} =$ $\frac{1}{2} =$ $\frac{1}{2}$

Row 2: $\frac{1}{2} + \frac{1}{4} =$ $\frac{2}{4} + \frac{1}{4} =$ $\frac{3}{4}$

Row 3: $\frac{1}{2} + \frac{1}{4} + \frac{1}{8} =$ $\frac{4}{8} + \frac{2}{8} + \frac{1}{8} =$ $\frac{7}{8}$

Row 4: $\frac{1}{2} + \frac{1}{4} + \frac{1}{8} + \frac{1}{16} =$ $\frac{8}{16} + \frac{4}{16} + \frac{2}{16} + \frac{1}{16} =$ $\frac{15}{16}$

1. What is the relationship between the denominators of the fractions in the first column?

2. What is the relationship between the numerators of the fractions in the second column?

3. In the space below, write Row 5 of the pattern.

4. What would be the fraction at the end of Row 6? Row 9?

5. Now complete the following pattern.

Row 1: $\frac{1}{3} =$ $\frac{1}{3} =$ $\frac{1}{3}$

Row 2: $\frac{1}{3} + \frac{1}{9} =$ $\frac{3}{9} + \frac{1}{9} =$ _____

Row 3: $\frac{1}{3} + \frac{1}{9} + \frac{1}{27} =$ _____ _____

Row 4: _____ _____ _____

Row 5: _____ _____ _____

6. **CHALLENGE** Find this sum: $\frac{1}{4} + \frac{1}{16} + \frac{1}{64} + \frac{1}{256} + \frac{1}{1,024} + \frac{1}{4,096}$

Enrichment Worksheet 8-4

Extending Problems

When examining the solution of a problem, good problem solvers look for ways to extend the problem. The questions on this page show you a way to examine and extend the following pattern.

Row 1: $\frac{1}{2} =$ $\frac{1}{2} =$ $\frac{1}{2}$

Row 2: $\frac{1}{2} + \frac{1}{4} =$ $\frac{2}{4} + \frac{1}{4} =$ $\frac{3}{4}$

Row 3: $\frac{1}{2} + \frac{1}{4} + \frac{1}{8} =$ $\frac{4}{8} + \frac{2}{8} + \frac{1}{8} =$ $\frac{7}{8}$

Row 4: $\frac{1}{2} + \frac{1}{4} + \frac{1}{8} + \frac{1}{16} =$ $\frac{8}{16} + \frac{4}{16} + \frac{2}{16} + \frac{1}{16} =$ $\frac{15}{16}$

1. What is the relationship between the denominators of the fractions in the first column?
Each denominator is multiplied by 2 to get the next one.

2. What is the relationship between the numerators of the fractions in the second column?
Each numerator is divided by 2 to get the next one.

3. In the space below, write Row 5 of the pattern.
$\frac{1}{2} + \frac{1}{4} + \frac{1}{8} + \frac{1}{16} + \frac{1}{32} = \frac{16}{32} + \frac{8}{32} + \frac{4}{32} + \frac{2}{32} + \frac{1}{32} = \frac{31}{32}$

4. What would be the fraction at the end of Row 6? Row 9?
$\frac{63}{64}; \frac{511}{512}$

5. Now complete the following pattern.

Row 1: $\frac{1}{3} =$ $\frac{1}{3} =$ $\frac{1}{3}$

Row 2: $\frac{1}{3} + \frac{1}{9} =$ $\frac{3}{9} + \frac{1}{9} =$ $\frac{4}{9}$

Row 3: $\frac{1}{3} + \frac{1}{9} + \frac{1}{27} =$ $\frac{9}{27} + \frac{3}{27} + \frac{1}{27} =$ $\frac{13}{27}$

Row 4: $\frac{1}{3} + \frac{1}{9} + \frac{1}{27} + \frac{1}{81} =$ $\frac{27}{81} + \frac{9}{81} + \frac{3}{81} + \frac{1}{81} =$ $\frac{40}{81}$

Row 5: $\frac{1}{3} + \frac{1}{9} + \frac{1}{27} + \frac{1}{81} + \frac{1}{243} =$ $\frac{81}{243} + \frac{27}{243} + \frac{9}{243} + \frac{3}{243} + \frac{1}{243} = \frac{121}{243}$

6. **CHALLENGE** Find this sum: $\frac{1}{4} + \frac{1}{16} + \frac{1}{64} + \frac{1}{256} + \frac{1}{1,024} + \frac{1}{4,096}$ $\frac{1,365}{4,096}$

Glencoe Division, Macmillan/McGraw-Hill

Enrichment Worksheet 8-5

Figurate Numbers

Figurate numbers are numbers associated with a pattern of geometric figures. For example, the diagram at the right shows the first four **triangular numbers.** The first number is 1, and then the pattern is *add 2, add 3, add 4, and so on.*

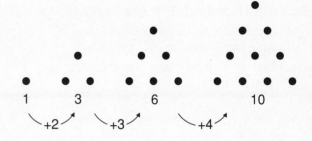

1. Refer to the diagram above. Find the next six triangular numbers.

1, 3, 6, 10,_____,_____,_____,_____,_____,_____

2. The diagram at the right represents the first four **square numbers.** What is the pattern? Use the pattern to list the first ten square numbers in the space below.

_____,_____,_____,_____,_____,_____,_____,_____,_____,_____

3. The diagram at the right represents the first four **rectangular numbers**. What is the pattern? Use the pattern to list the first ten rectangular numbers in the space below.

_____,_____,_____,_____,_____,_____,_____,_____,_____,_____

4. In the space below, sketch the geometric figure that represents the sixth rectangular number.

5. In the space below, sketch the geometric figure that represents the sixth triangular number.

Enrichment Worksheet 8-5

Figurate Numbers

Figurate numbers are numbers associated with a pattern of geometric figures. For example, the diagram at the right shows the first four **triangular numbers.** The first number is 1, and then the pattern is *add 2, add 3, add 4, and so on.*

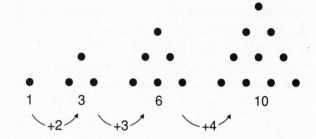

1. Refer to the diagram above. Find the next six triangular numbers.

   1, 3, 6, 10, __15__ , __21__ , __28__ , __36__ , __45__ , __55__

2. The diagram at the right represents the first four **square numbers.** What is the pattern? Use the pattern to list the first ten square numbers in the space below.
   add 3, add 5, add 7, and so on

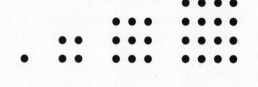

   __1__ , __4__ , __9__ , __16__ , __25__ , __36__ , __49__ , __64__ , __81__ , __100__

3. The diagram at the right represents the first four **rectangular numbers**. What is the pattern? Use the pattern to list the first ten rectangular numbers in the space below.
   add 4, add 6, add 8, and so on

   __2__ , __6__ , __12__ , __20__ , __30__ , __42__ , __56__ , __72__ , __90__ , __110__

4. In the space below, sketch the geometric figure that represents the sixth rectangular number.

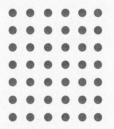

5. In the space below, sketch the geometric figure that represents the sixth triangular number.

Glencoe Division, Macmillan/McGraw-Hill

Enrichment Worksheet 8-6

Operations with Fractions and Decimals

Sometimes an operation involves both fractions and decimals. To perform the operation, you need to express all the numbers in the same form. Here are two examples.

$\frac{1}{5} \div 0.\overline{3} = \frac{1}{5} \div \frac{1}{3}$ ← Express the decimal as a fraction.

$\qquad = \frac{1}{5} \times \frac{3}{1}$

$\qquad = \frac{3}{5}$

$\frac{3}{4} + 0.115 = 0.75 + 0.115$ ← Express the fraction as a decimal.

$\qquad = 0.865$

Perform the operation. Express the answer as a fraction or mixed number in simplest form.

1. $\frac{5}{16} \div 0.25$

2. $0.\overline{6} \div \frac{7}{9}$

3. $0.125 \times \frac{4}{11}$

4. $1\frac{1}{5} \times 0.\overline{3}$

5. $0.8 - \frac{3}{5}$

6. $1\frac{3}{8} - 0.875$

Perform the operation. Express the answer as a decimal.

7. $0.34 \div \frac{1}{5}$

8. $\frac{1}{8} \div 0.005$

9. $0.001 \times \frac{3}{5}$

10. $6.39 + \frac{7}{8}$

11. $9.1 - \frac{1}{4}$

12. $\frac{3}{8} + 0.709 + \frac{2}{5}$

13. Kevin is making one recipe that calls for $1\frac{1}{4}$ pounds of hamburger and another that calls for 2 pounds. In the store, he finds a family pack of hamburger that is labeled 3.75 pounds. Is this more or less than he needs? How much more or less?

14. Daneesha needs $1\frac{1}{2}$ yards of material to make a jacket and $1\frac{3}{4}$ yards of material to make a skirt. The material costs $7.50 per yard. What is the total cost of the material for the skirt and jacket? (Round your answer to the nearest cent.)

Enrichment Worksheet 8-6

Operations with Fractions and Decimals

Sometimes an operation involves both fractions and decimals. To perform the operation, you need to express all the numbers in the same form. Here are two examples.

$\frac{1}{5} \div 0.\overline{3} = \frac{1}{5} \div \frac{1}{3}$ ← Express the decimal as a fraction.

$\quad = \frac{1}{5} \times \frac{3}{1}$

$\quad = \frac{3}{5}$

$\frac{3}{4} + 0.115 = 0.75 + 0.115$ ← Express the fraction as a decimal.

$\quad = 0.865$

Perform the operation. Express the answer as a fraction or mixed number in simplest form.

1. $\frac{5}{16} \div 0.25$ **$1\frac{1}{4}$**

2. $0.\overline{6} \div \frac{7}{9}$ **$\frac{6}{7}$**

3. $0.125 \times \frac{4}{11}$ **$\frac{1}{22}$**

4. $1\frac{1}{5} \times 0.\overline{3}$ **$\frac{2}{5}$**

5. $0.8 - \frac{3}{5}$ **$\frac{1}{5}$**

6. $1\frac{3}{8} - 0.875$ **$\frac{1}{2}$**

Perform the operation. Express the answer as a decimal.

7. $0.34 \div \frac{1}{5}$ **1.7**

8. $\frac{1}{8} \div 0.005$ **25**

9. $0.001 \times \frac{3}{5}$ **0.0006**

10. $6.39 + \frac{7}{8}$ **7.265**

11. $9.1 - \frac{1}{4}$ **8.85**

12. $\frac{3}{8} + 0.709 + \frac{2}{5}$ **1.484**

13. Kevin is making one recipe that calls for $1\frac{1}{4}$ pounds of hamburger and another that calls for 2 pounds. In the store, he finds a family pack of hamburger that is labeled 3.75 pounds. Is this more or less than he needs? How much more or less?
more; $\frac{1}{2}$ pound

14. Daneesha needs $1\frac{1}{2}$ yards of material to make a jacket and $1\frac{3}{4}$ yards of material to make a skirt. The material costs $7.50 per yard. What is the total cost of the material for the skirt and jacket? (Round your answer to the nearest cent.) **$24.38**

Enrichment Worksheet 8-7

Modeling Division of Fractions on a Ruler

How many half-inch lengths are in 4 inches? When you look
at a ruler, it is easy to see that the answer is 8.

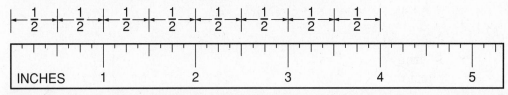

So, this diagram is also a model for the division $4 \div \frac{1}{2} = 8$.

Write the division that is modeled in each diagram.

1.

2.

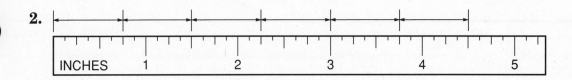

3.

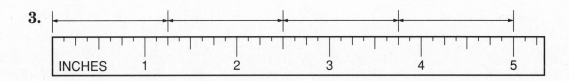

4.

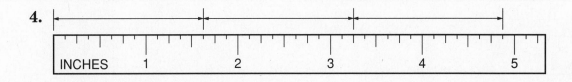

5. Use the ruler below. Create a model for the division $4\frac{2}{3} \div \frac{2}{3} = 7$.

INCHES	1	2	3	4	5

Enrichment Worksheet 8-7

Modeling Division of Fractions on a Ruler

How many half-inch lengths are in 4 inches? When you look
at a ruler, it is easy to see that the answer is 8.

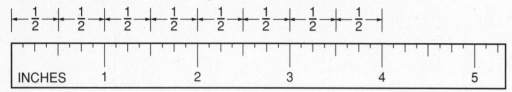

So, this diagram is also a model for the division $4 \div \frac{1}{2} = 8$.

Write the division that is modeled in each diagram.

1. 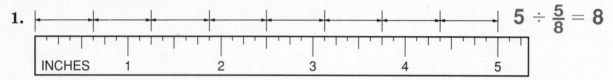 $5 \div \frac{5}{8} = 8$

2. 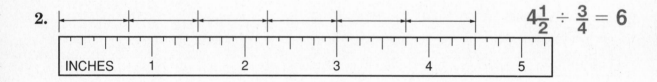 $4\frac{1}{2} \div \frac{3}{4} = 6$

3. 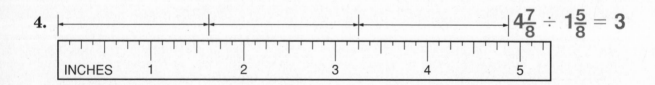 $5 \div 1\frac{1}{4} = 4$

4. 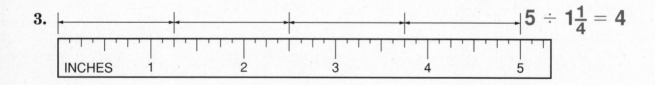 $4\frac{7}{8} \div 1\frac{5}{8} = 3$

5. Use the ruler below. Create a model for the division $4\frac{2}{3} \div \frac{2}{3} = 7$.

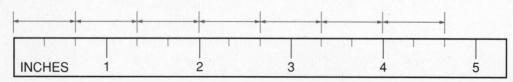

Enrichment Worksheet 8-8

Relating Customary and Metric Units

Both customary and metric measurements are used in the
United States. Therefore, it is a good idea to develop some
sense of the relationships between the two systems. Here
are some *rules of thumb* that are commonly used.

> An inch is about equal to 2.5 centimeters.
> A yard is a little less than 1 meter.
> A mile is a little more than 1.5 kilometers.
> A kilogram is a little more than 2 pounds.
> A liter is a little less than 1 quart.

**Use the relationships given above. Tell whether each
statement is true or false.**

1. A length of 4 meters is longer than 4 yards.

2. A weight of 10 pounds is more than 5 kilograms.

3. A capacity of 1 gallon is more than 4 liters.

4. A length of 1 foot is about the same as 30 centimeters.

5. A kilometer is more than half a mile.

6. A pound is a little more than half a kilogram.

7. On a road in Canada, the posted
   speed limit is 45 kilometers per
   hour. Aimée is driving at a speed
   of 40 miles per hour. Is this above
   or below the speed limit?

8. Sean has a recipe that calls for
   0.25 L of milk. He has a one-cup
   container of milk in the
   refrigerator. Is this enough milk
   for the recipe?

9. The posted load limit for a bridge is
   5 tons. The mass of Darryl's truck
   is 1,500 kilograms, and it is holding
   cargo that weighs a half ton. Can
   Darryl drive his truck across the
   bridge?

10. Leah is pouring paint from a
    5-gallon can into some jars. She
    has twelve jars that each hold
    1 liter and six jars that each hold
    1.25 liters. Does she have enough
    jars for all the paint?

Enrichment Worksheet 8-8

Relating Customary and Metric Units

Both customary and metric measurements are used in the United States. Therefore, it is a good idea to develop some sense of the relationships between the two systems. Here are some *rules of thumb* that are commonly used.

> An inch is about equal to 2.5 centimeters.
> A yard is a little less than 1 meter.
> A mile is a little more than 1.5 kilometers.
> A kilogram is a little more than 2 pounds.
> A liter is a little less than 1 quart.

Use the relationships given above. Tell whether each statement is true or false.

1. A length of 4 meters is longer than 4 yards. **true**

2. A weight of 10 pounds is more than 5 kilograms. **false**

3. A capacity of 1 gallon is more than 4 liters. **true**

4. A length of 1 foot is about the same as 30 centimeters. **true**

5. A kilometer is more than half a mile. **true**

6. A pound is a little more than half a kilogram. **false**

7. On a road in Canada, the posted speed limit is 45 kilometers per hour. Aimée is driving at a speed of 40 miles per hour. Is this above or below the speed limit? **above**

8. Sean has a recipe that calls for 0.25 L of milk. He has a one-cup container of milk in the refrigerator. Is this enough milk for the recipe? **yes**

9. The posted load limit for a bridge is 5 tons. The mass of Darryl's truck is 1,500 kilograms, and it is holding cargo that weighs a half ton. Can Darryl drive his truck across the bridge? **yes**

10. Leah is pouring paint from a 5-gallon can into some jars. She has twelve jars that each hold 1 liter and six jars that each hold 1.25 liters. Does she have enough jars for all the paint? **no**

Enrichment Worksheet 9-1

Clock-Watching

You probably don't have to look far to find an everyday model for an angle. Just look at a clock like the one at the right, and think of the hour and minute hands as the sides of an angle. Here's how you can find the measure of the angle at 1:00.

There are 360° in a circle.
There are 12 evenly-spaced hours on the clock face.
$$360° \div 12 = 30°$$

So, the measure of the angle at 1:00 is 30°.

Find the measure of the angle formed by the hands of the clock at each hour.

1. 2:00   **2.** 5:00   **3.** 8:00

4. 11:00   **5.** 3:00   **6.** 9:00

7. List all the hours when the hands of the clock form an obtuse angle.

8. How many hours are there when the hands of the clock form an acute angle?

9. A **straight angle** measures 180°. At what hour do the hands of the clock form a straight angle?

10. What is the measure of the angle formed by the hands of the clock at 12:00?

11. How many times between 1:00 and 2:00 do the hands of the clock form a right angle?

12. CHALLENGE How many times each day do the hands of the clock form a right angle?

Enrichment Worksheet 9-1

Clock-Watching

You probably don't have to look far to find an everyday model for an angle. Just look at a clock like the one at the right, and think of the hour and minute hands as the sides of an angle. Here's how you can find the measure of the angle at 1:00.

There are 360° in a circle.
There are 12 evenly-spaced hours on the clock face.
$$360° ÷ 12 = 30°$$

So, the measure of the angle at 1:00 is 30°.

Find the measure of the angle formed by the hands of the clock at each hour.

1. 2:00   **60°**

2. 5:00   **150°**

3. 8:00   **120°**

4. 11:00   **30°**

5. 3:00   **90°**

6. 9:00   **90°**

7. List all the hours when the hands of the clock form an obtuse angle.   **4:00, 5:00, 7:00, 8:00**

8. How many hours are there when the hands of the clock form an acute angle?   **four**

9. A **straight angle** measures 180°. At what hour do the hands of the clock form a straight angle?   **6:00**

10. What is the measure of the angle formed by the hands of the clock at 12:00?   **0°**

11. How many times between 1:00 and 2:00 do the hands of the clock form a right angle?   **two**

12. **CHALLENGE** How many times each day do the hands of the clock form a right angle?   **forty-eight**

Enrichment Worksheet 9-2

Compass Directions

When a plane is in flight, its directions is expressed as an angle measure. One method of doing this is to give the measure of the angle formed by the plane's flight path and one of the directions of the compass—north, east, south, or west. For example, this is how you express the two flight paths shown in the figure at the right.

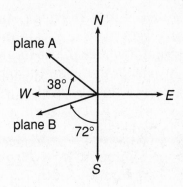

    plane A: west 38° north, or W 38° N
    plane B: south 72° west, or S 72° W

Write an expression for the direction of each flight path. (You will need to measure the angle with your protractor.)

1.

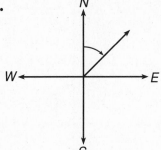

2.

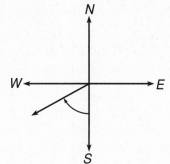

3.

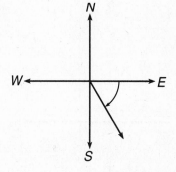

Use your protractor to draw each flight path.

4. E 70° S

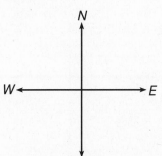

5. E 51° N

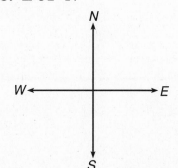

6. W 75° N

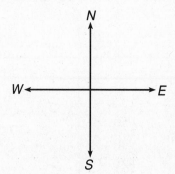

7. *CHALLENGE* The **bearing** of a plane is the measure of the angle between its flight path and due north, measured in a clockwise direction. For example, in the figure at the top of the page, the bearing of plane A is 90° + 90° + 72° = 252°. Give the bearing for each flight path in Exercises 1-6.

Name _____ **Date** _____

Enrichment Worksheet 9-2

Compass Directions

When a plane is in flight, its directions is expressed as an angle measure. One method of doing this is to give the measure of the angle formed by the plane's flight path and one of the directions of the compass—north, east, south, or west. For example, this is how you express the two flight paths shown in the figure at the right.

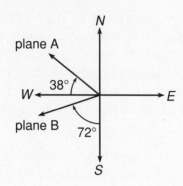

plane A: west 38° north, or W 38° N
plane B: south 72° west, or S 72° W

Write an expression for the direction of each flight path. (You will need to measure the angle with your protractor.)

1.

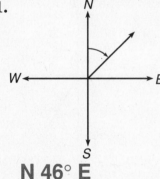

N 46° E

2.

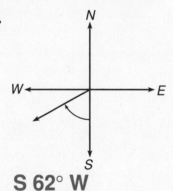

S 62° W

3.

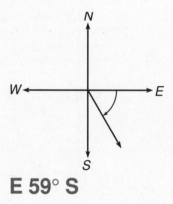

E 59° S

Use your protractor to draw each flight path.

4. E 70° S

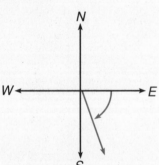

5. E 51° N

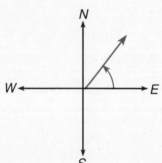

6. W 75° N

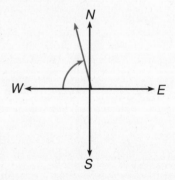

7. *CHALLENGE* The **bearing** of a plane is the measure of the angle between its flight path and due north, measured in a clockwise direction. For example, in the figure at the top of the page, the bearing of plane A is 90° + 90° + 72° = 252°. Give the bearing for each flight path in Exercises 1-6.

46°, 207°, 149°, 160°, 141°, 345°

Enrichment Worksheet 9-3

Line Designs

Line designs are a type of optical illusion—they look like curves, but they are made up entirely of line segments. This is the basic method for making a line design.

Draw two congruent segments that meet at an endpoint.

Mark off smaller congruent segments. Label them as shown.

Connect point A to point A, point B to point B, and so on.

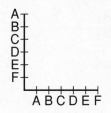

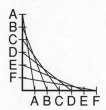

Complete each line design.

1.

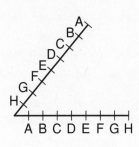

2.

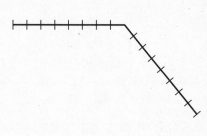

3.

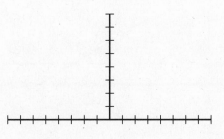

4.

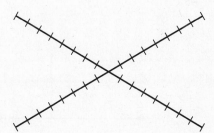

5. CHALLENGE On a separate sheet of paper, make a large copy of each of these figures. Then complete the line design.

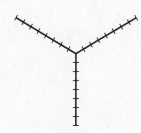

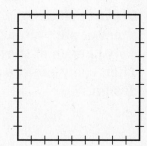

Enrichment Worksheet 9-3

Line Designs

Line designs are a type of optical illusion—they look like curves, but they are made up entirely of line segments. This is the basic method for making a line design.

Draw two congruent segments that meet at an endpoint.

Mark off smaller congruent segments. Label them as shown.

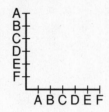

Connect point A to point A, point B to point B, and so on.

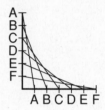

Complete each line design.

1.

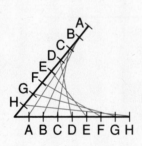

2.

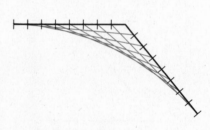

3.

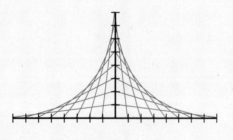

4.

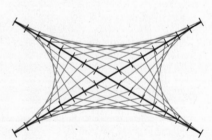

5. CHALLENGE On a separate sheet of paper, make a large copy of each of these figures. Then complete the line design.

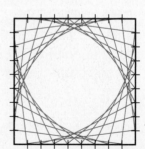

Enrichment Worksheet 9-4

Creative Constructions

The compass and straightedge are very simple
tools, yet they can be used to create some very
complex and beautiful designs. It might surprise
you to know that the designs on this page involve
nothing more complicated than bisecting segments
and angles! For instance, the outline of the design
at the right was created in just four steps.

Step 1   Step 2   Step 3   Step 4

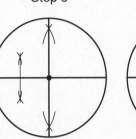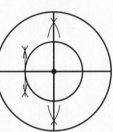

Construct a copy of each design in the empty circle.

1.

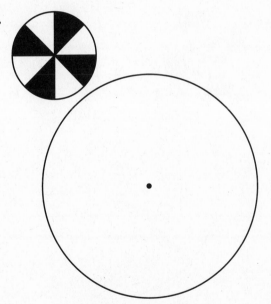

2.

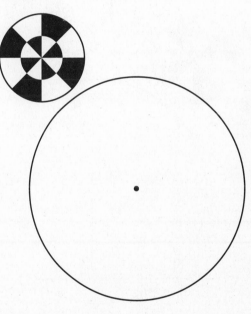

Construct a copy of each design on a separate sheet of paper.

3.    **4.**    **5.**

Enrichment Worksheet 9-4

Creative Constructions

The compass and straightedge are very simple tools, yet they can be used to create some very complex and beautiful designs. It might surprise you to know that the designs on this page involve nothing more complicated than bisecting segments and angles! For instance, the outline of the design at the right was created in just four steps.

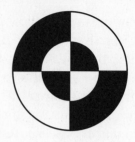

| Step 1 | Step 2 | Step 3 | Step 4 |

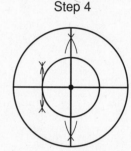

Construct a copy of each design in the empty circle.

Check students' drawings.

1.

2.

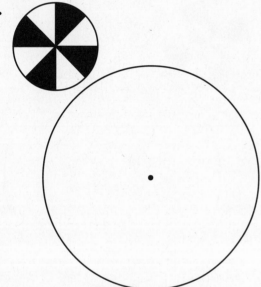

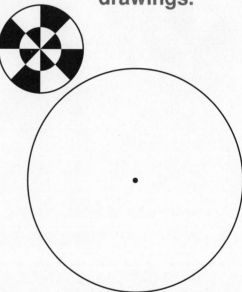

Construct a copy of each design on a separate sheet of paper.

3.    4.    5.

Enrichment Worksheet 9-5

Making Conjectures

A **conjecture** is an educated guess or an opinion. Mathematicians and scientists often make conjectures when they observe patterns in a collection of data. On this page, you will be asked to make a conjecture about polygons.

$89° + 107° + 121° + 43°$
$= 360°$

Use a protractor to measure the angles of each polygon. Then find the sum of the measures. (Use the quadrilateral at the right as an example.)

1.

2.

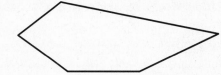

3.

4.

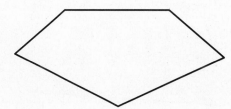

5.

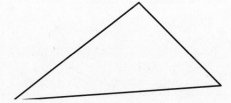

6.

7. Make a conjecture. How is the sum of the angle measures of a polygon related to the number of sides?

8. Test your conjecture. On a clean sheet of paper, use a straightedge to draw a hexagon. What do you guess is the sum of the angle measures? Measure each angle and find the sum. Was your conjecture true?

Enrichment Worksheet 9-5

Making Conjectures

A **conjecture** is an educated guess or an opinion. Mathematicians and scientists often make conjectures when they observe patterns in a collection of data. On this page, you will be asked to make a conjecture about polygons.

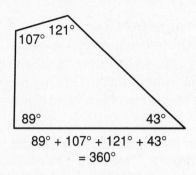

$$89° + 107° + 121° + 43°$$
$$= 360°$$

Use a protractor to measure the angles of each polygon. Then find the sum of the measures. (Use the quadrilateral at the right as an example.)

1.

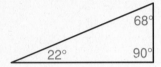

sum = **180°**

2.

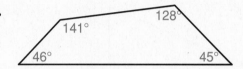

sum = **360°**

3.

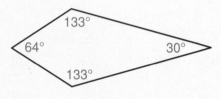

sum = **360°**

4.

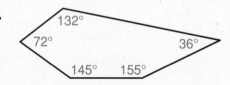

sum = **540°**

5.

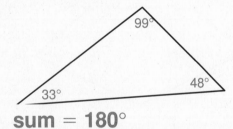

sum = **180°**

6.

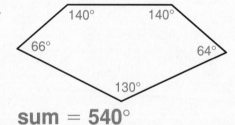

sum = **540°**

Answers will vary.

7. **Make a conjecture.** How is the sum of the angle measures of a polygon related to the number of sides?
When the number of sides increases by 1, the sum of the angle measures increases by 180°.

8. **Test your conjecture.** On a clean sheet of paper, use a straightedge to draw a hexagon. What do you guess is the sum of the angle measures? Measure each angle and find the sum. Was your conjecture true?
Conjectures will vary. The sum of the angle measures is 720°.

Enrichment Worksheet 9-6

Number Patterns in Geometry

At the right is a pattern of geometric figures. What is the area of the eighth figure in the pattern? Counting the square units, you see a number pattern: *add 2 to each number.* So, to find the area of the eighth figure, continue the number pattern until you come to the eighth number.

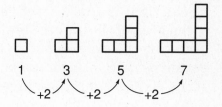

The area of the eighth figure is 15 square units.

1. Refer to the pattern at the right.
   a. What is the area of the ninth figure?

   b. What is the *perimeter* of the seventh figure?

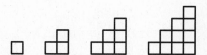

2. At the right, you see a pattern of figures made up of triangles.
   a. How many small triangles (△) are in the sixth figure?

   b. What is the perimeter of the eighth figure?

Draw the next figure in each pattern.

3.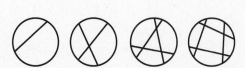

4.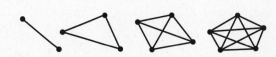

5.

6.

Enrichment Worksheet 9-6

Number Patterns in Geometry

At the right is a pattern of geometric figures. What
is the area of the eighth figure in the pattern?
Counting the square units, you see a number
pattern: *add 2 to each number*. So, to find the area
of the eighth figure, continue the number pattern
until you come to the eighth number.

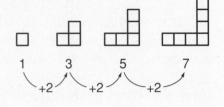

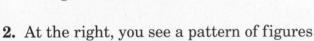

The area of the eighth figure is 15 square
units.

1. Refer to the pattern at the right.
   a. What is the area of the ninth figure?
   45 square units
   b. What is the *perimeter* of the seventh
   figure? **28 units**

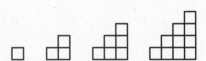

2. At the right, you see a pattern of figures
   made up of triangles.
   a. How many small triangles (△) are in the
   sixth figure?   **36**

   b. What is the perimeter of the eighth
   figure? **24 units**

Draw the next figure in each pattern.

3.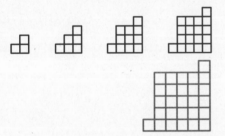

...

3.

4.

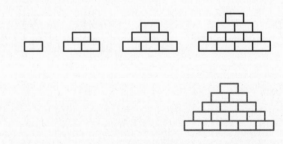

5.

6.

Enrichment Worksheet 9-7

Alphabet Symmetry

In their work, artists and designers must often consider the symmetries of letters. For instance, you see at the right that the capital letter **A** has one line of symmetry, which is vertical.

1. Draw all lines of symmetry for each letter. If a letter has no line of symmetry, write *none*.

B C D E F

G H I J K

L M N O P

Q R S T U

V W X Y Z

2. The entire word HOE has a horizontal line of symmetry.

◄HOE►

Find at least two other words like HOE. What is the longest such word you can find?

3. When you write the word YOU vertically, as shown at the right, the entire word has a vertical line of symmetry. Find at least two other words like YOU. What is the longest such word you can find?

4. **CHALLENGE** Can you find a word that has both horizontal symmetry, like HOE, and vertical symmetry, like YOU?

Enrichment Worksheet 9-7

Alphabet Symmetry

In their work, artists and designers must often consider the symmetries of letters. For instance, you see at the right that the capital letter **A** has one line of symmetry, which is vertical.

1. Draw all lines of symmetry for each letter. If a letter has no line of symmetry, write *none*.

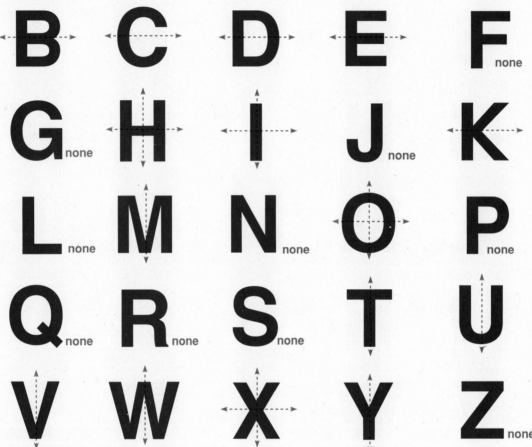

2. The entire word HOE has a horizontal line of symmetry.

    ‹-HOE-›

    Find at least two other words like HOE. What is the longest such word you can find?
    Samples: HIDE, COOKBOOK

3. When you write the word YOU vertically, as shown at the right, the entire word has a vertical line of symmetry. Find at least two other words like YOU. What is the longest such word you can find? **Samples: MOUTH, WHOM**

4. *CHALLENGE* Can you find a word that has both horizontal symmetry, like HOE, and vertical symmetry, like YOU?
HI, OX, OHIO

Glencoe Division, Macmillan/McGraw-Hill

Enrichment Worksheet 9-8

Reptiles

The word **reptiles** stands for <u>rep</u>eating <u>tiles</u>. A geometric figure is a reptile if it can be divided into smaller parts according to these rules.

1. All the smaller parts must be *congruent* to each other.
2. All the smaller parts must be *similar* to the original tile.

Here are two examples of figures that are reptiles.

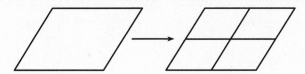 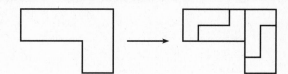

Divide each reptile into four congruent parts.

1.

2.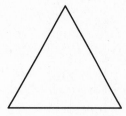

3.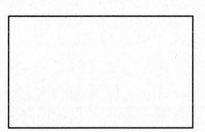

4.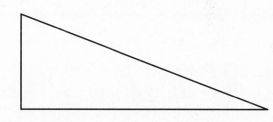

5.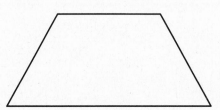

6.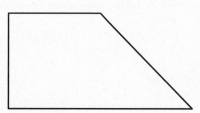

7. *CHALLENGE*   Show how to use four figures like the one at the right to make a reptile.

Reptiles

The word **reptiles** stands for <u>rep</u>eating <u>tiles</u>. A geometric figure
is a reptile if it can be divided into smaller parts according to
these rules.

   1. All the smaller parts must be *congruent* to each other.
   2. All the smaller parts must be *similar* to the original tile.

Here are two examples of figures that are reptiles.

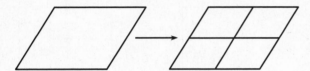
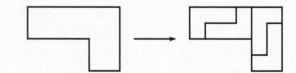

Divide each reptile into four congruent parts.

1.
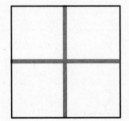

2.
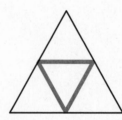

3.
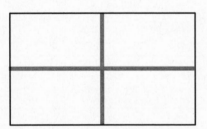

4.
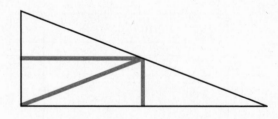

5.
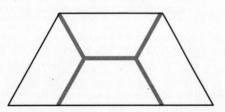

6.
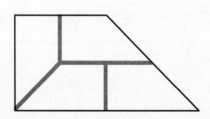

7. *CHALLENGE*   Show how to use
   four figures like the one at the
   right to make a reptile.

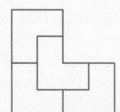

Enrichment Worksheet 10-1

Ratios and Rectangles

1. Use a centimeter ruler to measure the width and the length of each rectangle. Then express the ratio of the width to the length as a fraction in simplest form.

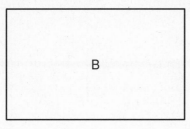

A

B

C

D

E

2. Similar figures have the same shape, but not necessarily the same size. Two rectangles are similar if the ratio of the width to the length is the same for each. Which rectangles in Exercise 1 are similar?

3. For centuries, artists and architects have used a shape called the **golden rectangle** because people seem to find it most pleasant to look at. In a golden rectangle, the ratio of the width to the length is a little less than $\frac{5}{8}$. Which rectangle in Exercise 1 is most nearly a golden rectangle?

Enrichment Worksheet 10-1

Ratios and Rectangles

1. Use a centimeter ruler to measure the width and the length of each rectangle. Then express the ratio of the width to the length as a fraction in simplest form.

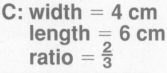

C: width = 4 cm
length = 6 cm
ratio = $\frac{2}{3}$

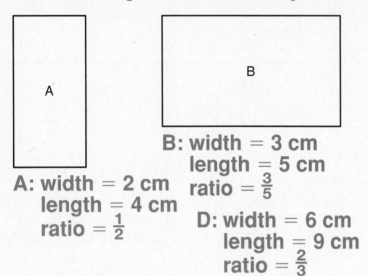

A: width = 2 cm
length = 4 cm
ratio = $\frac{1}{2}$

B: width = 3 cm
length = 5 cm
ratio = $\frac{3}{5}$

D: width = 6 cm
length = 9 cm
ratio = $\frac{2}{3}$

E: width = 4.8 cm
length = 4.8 cm
ratio = $\frac{1}{1}$

2. Similar figures have the same shape, but not necessarily the same size. Two rectangles are similar if the ratio of the width to the length is the same for each. Which rectangles in Exercise 1 are similar? **C and D**

3. For centuries, artists and architects have used a shape called the **golden rectangle** because people seem to find it most pleasant to look at. In a golden rectangle, the ratio of the width to the length is a little less than $\frac{5}{8}$. Which rectangle in Exercise 1 is most nearly a golden rectangle? **B**

Enrichment Worksheet 10-2

Using Proportions to Change Units of Measure

When you need to change units of measure—gallons to quarts, ounces to pounds, and so on—do you sometimes forget whether to multiply or divide? Almost everyone gets confused at one time or another, and so it is a good idea to learn an alternative method. Whether you are changing from smaller to larger units or from larger to smaller, you can start by writing a proportion. Here's how.

14 gal = _?_ qt

Use the fact that 1 gal = 4 qt.

gallons → $\frac{1}{4} = \frac{14}{q}$ ← gallons
quarts →   ← quarts

$1 \times q = 4 \times 14$

$q = 56$

So, 14 gal = 56 qt.

14 qt = _?_ gal

gallons → $\frac{1}{4} = \frac{g}{14}$ ← gallons
quarts →   ← quarts

$1 \times 14 = 4 \times g$

$14 = 4g$

$3\frac{1}{2} = 1g$

So, 14 qt = $3\frac{1}{2}$ gal.

Write a proportion that can be used to change each measurement.

1. 24 ft = _?_ in.

2. 24 in. = _?_ ft

3. 54 oz = _?_ lb

4. 16 c = _?_ fl oz

5. 7 cm = _?_ m

6. 14 L = _?_ mL

Complete.

7. 6 yd = _____ ft

8. 9 pt = _____ qt

9. 12 oz = _____ lb

10. $5\frac{1}{2}$ qt = _____ pt

11. 49 km = _____ m

12. 6.5 L = _____ mL

13. 850 mg = _____ g

14. 9.1 mm = _____ cm

Enrichment Worksheet 10-2

Using Proportions to Change Units of Measure

When you need to change units of measure—gallons to quarts, ounces to pounds, and so on—do you sometimes forget whether to multiply or divide? Almost everyone gets confused at one time or another, and so it is a good idea to learn an alternative method. Whether you are changing from smaller to larger units or from larger to smaller, you can start by writing a proportion. Here's how.

14 gal = $\underline{\ ?\ }$ qt

Use the fact that 1 gal = 4 qt.

gallons → $\frac{1}{4} = \frac{14}{q}$ ← gallons
quarts → $\quad$ ← quarts

$1 \times q = 4 \times 14$

$q = 56$

So, 14 gal = 56 qt.

---

14 qt = $\underline{\ ?\ }$ gal

gallons → $\frac{1}{4} = \frac{g}{14}$ ← gallons
quarts → $\quad$ ← quarts

$1 \times 14 = 4 \times g$

$14 = 4g$

$3\frac{1}{2} = 1g$

So, 14 qt = $3\frac{1}{2}$ gal.

Write a proportion that can be used to change each measurement.

1. 24 ft = $\underline{\ ?\ }$ in. $\frac{1}{12} = \frac{24}{i}$

2. 24 in. = $\underline{\ ?\ }$ ft $\frac{1}{12} = \frac{f}{24}$

3. 54 oz = $\underline{\ ?\ }$ lb $\frac{1}{16} = \frac{p}{54}$

4. 16 c = $\underline{\ ?\ }$ fl oz $\frac{1}{8} = \frac{16}{f}$

5. 7 cm = $\underline{\ ?\ }$ m $\frac{1}{100} = \frac{m}{7}$

6. 14 L = $\underline{\ ?\ }$ mL $\frac{1}{1,000} = \frac{14}{m}$

Complete.

7. 6 yd = $\underline{\ 18\ }$ ft

8. 9 pt = $\underline{\ 4\frac{1}{2}\ }$ qt

9. 12 oz = $\underline{\ \frac{3}{4}\ }$ lb

10. $5\frac{1}{2}$ qt = $\underline{\ 11\ }$ pt

11. 49 km = $\underline{\ 49,000\ }$ m

12. 6.5 L = $\underline{\ 6,500\ }$ mL

13. 850 mg = $\underline{\ 0.85\ }$ g

14. 9.1 mm = $\underline{\ 0.91\ }$ cm

Enrichment Worksheet 10-3

Counting Handshakes

Sometimes, drawing a diagram is just one of many strategies that you use when solving a problem. On this page, you will see how several strategies are used in solving this problem.

At a party, twelve people are introduced to each other. Each person shakes hands with each of the others exactly once. How many handshakes are there in all?

1. *Solve a simpler problem.*

If there were only four people, you could use a diagram like the one at the right to picture all the handshakes. How many handshakes are there?

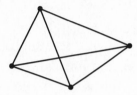

2. *Collect data.*

Use the strategy of drawing a diagram to solve a series of simpler problems. Enter your data in this chart.

Number of People	1	2	3	4	5
Diagram					
Number of Handshakes					

3. *Look for a pattern.*

a. Refer to the chart in Exercise 2. What pattern do you see in the row titled *number of handshakes*?

b. Write the first twelve terms of the pattern.

——, ——, ——, ——, ——, ——, ——, ——, ——, ——, ——, ——

c. How many handshakes are there among twelve people?

4. *Extend the problem.*

Each person at a party shakes hands with each other person exactly once. In all, there are 120 handshakes. How many people are at the party?

Enrichment Worksheet 10-3

Counting Handshakes

Sometimes, drawing a diagram is just one of many strategies that you use when solving a problem. On this page, you will see how several strategies are used in solving this problem.

At a party, twelve people are introduced to each other. Each person shakes hands with each of the others exactly once. How many handshakes are there in all?

1. *Solve a simpler problem.*

If there were only four people, you could use a diagram like the one at the right to picture all the handshakes. How many handshakes are there? **6**

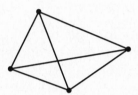

2. *Collect data.*

Use the strategy of drawing a diagram to solve a series of simpler problems. Enter your data in this chart.

Number of People	1	2	3	4	5
Diagram	•	/	△	◁	⬠
Number of Handshakes	0	1	3	6	10

3. *Look for a pattern.*

a. Refer to the chart in Exercise 2. What pattern do you see in the row titled *number of handshakes*?
add 1, add 2, add 3, add 4, and so on

b. Write the first twelve terms of the pattern.
 0, **1**, **3**, **6**, **10**, **15**, **21**, **28**, **36**, **45**, **55**, **66**

c. How many handshakes are there among twelve people? **66**

4. *Extend the problem.*

Each person at a party shakes hands with each other person exactly once. In all, there are 120 handshakes. How many people are at the party? **16**

Enrichment Worksheet 10-4

Planning a Room

Before moving furniture into a room, many people plan an arrangment by making a scale drawing. This makes it possible to find the best arrangement for the room without actually moving heavy furniture.

For each piece of furniture, actual measurements are given. Compute scale measurements using the scale $\frac{1}{2}$ inch = 1 foot.

1. bed: $6\frac{1}{2}$ feet long, 3 feet wide

2. bedside table: $1\frac{1}{2}$ feet long, $1\frac{1}{2}$ feet wide

3. bookcase: $3\frac{1}{2}$ feet long, 1 foot wide

4. desk: 42 inches long, 18 inches wide

5. chest of drawers: 39 inches long, 18 inches wide

6. Use your answers from Exercises 1-5. Show how the furniture might be arranged in the bedroom shown below.

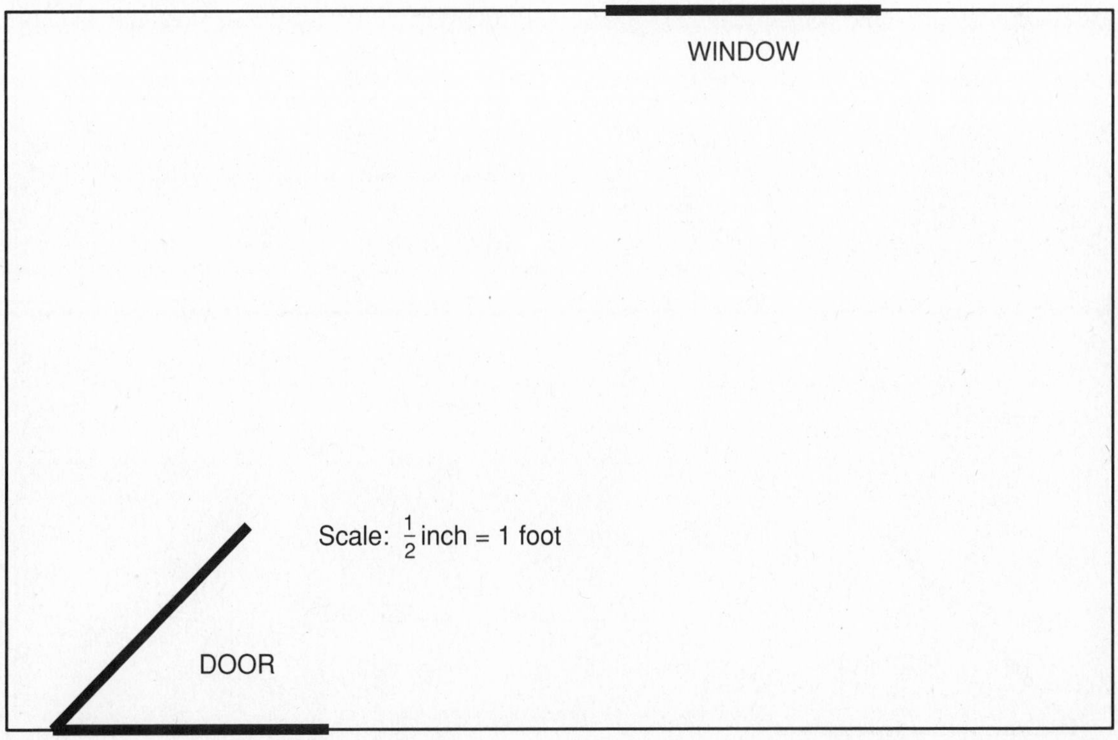

WINDOW

Scale: $\frac{1}{2}$ inch = 1 foot

DOOR

Enrichment Worksheet 10-4

Planning a Room

Before moving furniture into a room, many people plan an arrangment by making a scale drawing. This makes it possible to find the best arrangement for the room without actually moving heavy furniture.

For each piece of furniture, actual measurements are given.
Compute scale measurements using the scale $\frac{1}{2}$ inch = 1 foot.

1. bed: $6\frac{1}{2}$ feet long, 3 feet wide $3\frac{1}{4}$ **inches long, $1\frac{1}{2}$ inches wide**

2. bedside table: $1\frac{1}{2}$ feet long, $1\frac{1}{2}$ feet wide $\frac{3}{4}$ **inch long, $\frac{3}{4}$ inch wide**

3. bookcase: $3\frac{1}{2}$ feet long, 1 foot wide $1\frac{3}{4}$ **inches long, $\frac{1}{2}$ inch wide**

4. desk: 42 inches long, 18 inches wide $1\frac{3}{4}$ **inches long, $\frac{3}{4}$ inch wide**

5. chest of drawers: 39 inches long, 18 inches wide $1\frac{5}{8}$ **inches long, $\frac{3}{4}$ inch wide**

6. Use your answers from Exercises 1-5. Show how the furniture might be arranged in the bedroom shown below.

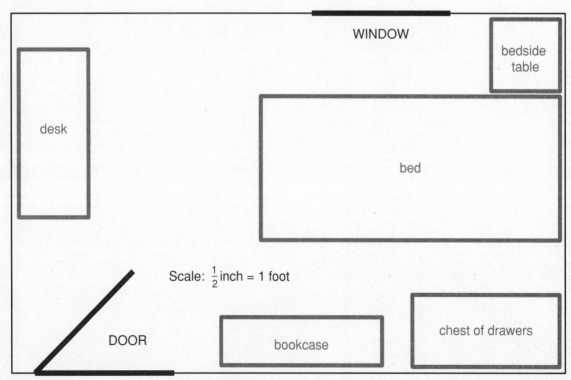

Scale: $\frac{1}{2}$ inch = 1 foot

Arrangements may vary.

Enrichment Worksheet 10-5

Percent and the Hundred Chart

The chart at the right shows all the whole numbers from 1 through 100.

This page challenges you to connect percents to what you know about number theory—factors, multiples, divisibility, and so on. Whenever you can, use a pattern in the chart to make your work easier.

For example, the multiples of 5 make up two columns of the chart —the fifth column and the tenth. So, 20 out of 100 numbers, or 20% of the numbers, are multiples of 5.

1	2	3	4	5	6	7	8	9	10
11	12	13	14	15	16	17	18	19	20
21	22	23	24	25	26	27	28	29	30
31	32	33	34	35	36	37	38	39	40
41	42	43	44	45	46	47	48	49	50
51	52	53	54	55	56	57	58	59	60
61	62	63	64	65	66	67	68	69	70
71	72	73	74	75	76	77	78	79	80
81	82	83	84	85	86	87	88	89	90
91	92	93	94	95	96	97	98	99	100

Use the hundred chart above. Find the percent of the numbers that:

1. are even numbers.

2. are odd numbers.

3. are multiples of 9.

4. are multiples of 11.

5. are divisible by 5.

6. are divisible by 3.

7. are divisible by 2 *and* divisible by 5.

8. are divisible by 2 *and* divisible by 3.

9. contain only even digits.

10. contain only odd digits.

11. have digits whose sum is 10.

12. have digits whose sum is 5.

13. contain the digit 0.

14. contain the digit 5.

15. are factors of 100.

16. are factors of 101.

17. are prime.

18. are composite.

Glencoe Division, Macmillan/McGraw-Hill

Enrichment Worksheet 10-5

Percent and the Hundred Chart

The chart at the right shows all the whole numbers from 1 through 100.

This page challenges you to connect percents to what you know about number theory— factors, multiples, divisibility, and so on. Whenever you can, use a pattern in the chart to make your work easier.

For example, the multiples of 5 make up two columns of the chart —the fifth column and the tenth. So, 20 out of 100 numbers, or 20% of the numbers, are multiples of 5.

1	2	3	4	5	6	7	8	9	10
11	12	13	14	15	16	17	18	19	20
21	22	23	24	25	26	27	28	29	30
31	32	33	34	35	36	37	38	39	40
41	42	43	44	45	46	47	48	49	50
51	52	53	54	55	56	57	58	59	60
61	62	63	64	65	66	67	68	69	70
71	72	73	74	75	76	77	78	79	80
81	82	83	84	85	86	87	88	89	90
91	92	93	94	95	96	97	98	99	100

Use the hundred chart above. Find the percent of the numbers that:

1. are even numbers. **50%**　　　　2. are odd numbers. **50%**

3. are multiples of 9. **11%**　　　　4. are multiples of 11. **9%**

5. are divisible by 5. **20%**　　　　6. are divisible by 3. **33%**

7. are divisible by 2 *and* divisible by 5.
10%

8. are divisible by 2 *and* divisible by 3.
16%

9. contain only even digits. **24%**　　　　10. contain only odd digits. **30%**

11. have digits whose sum is 10. **9%**　　　　12. have digits whose sum is 5. **6%**

13. contain the digit 0. **10%**　　　　14. contain the digit 5. **19%**

15. are factors of 100. **9%**　　　　16. are factors of 101. **1%**

17. are prime. **25%**　　　　18. are composite. **74%**

Enrichment Worksheet 10-6

Percent and Per Mill

A percent is a ratio that compares a number to 100.

$$\frac{83}{100} = 83 \text{ percent} = 83\% = 0.83$$

A ratio that compares a number to 1,000 is called a **per mill**. Just like percent, the ratio *per mill* has a special symbol, ‰.

$$\frac{83}{1,000} = 83 \text{ per mill} = 83‰ = 0.083$$

Throughout the world, the ratio that is used most commonly is percent. However, in some countries, you will find both ratios in use.

Express each per mill as a decimal.

1. 325‰

2. 71‰

3. 6‰

4. 900‰

5. 20‰

6. 100‰

Express each per mill as a fraction in simplest form.

7. 47‰

8. 400‰

9. 100‰

10. 25‰

11. 150‰

12. 30‰

Express each fraction as a per mill.

13. $\frac{729}{1,000}$

14. $\frac{58}{100}$

15. $\frac{7}{10}$

16. $\frac{1}{2}$

17. $\frac{3}{4}$

18. $\frac{5}{8}$

19. $\frac{4}{5}$

20. $\frac{17}{20}$

21. $\frac{1}{3}$

22. **CHALLENGE**   In the United States, you will sometimes find the **mill** used as a monetary unit. What amount of money do you think is represented by 1 mill?

Glencoe Division, Macmillan/McGraw-Hill

Enrichment Worksheet 10-6

Percent and Per Mill

A percent is a ratio that compares a number to 100.

$$\frac{83}{100} = 83 \text{ percent} = 83\% = 0.83$$

A ratio that compares a number to 1,000 is called a **per mill**. Just like percent, the ratio *per mill* has a special symbol, ‰.

$$\frac{83}{1,000} = 83 \text{ per mill} = 83‰ = 0.083$$

Throughout the world, the ratio that is used most commonly is percent. However, in some countries, you will find both ratios in use.

Express each per mill as a decimal.

1. 325‰ **0.325**
2. 71‰ **0.071**
3. 6‰ **0.006**

4. 900‰ **0.9**
5. 20‰ **0.02**
6. 100‰ **0.1**

Express each per mill as a fraction in simplest form.

7. 47‰ $\frac{47}{1,000}$
8. 400‰ $\frac{2}{5}$
9. 100‰ $\frac{1}{10}$

10. 25‰ $\frac{1}{40}$
11. 150‰ $\frac{3}{20}$
12. 30‰ $\frac{3}{100}$

Express each fraction as a per mill.

13. $\frac{729}{1,000}$ **729‰**
14. $\frac{58}{100}$ **580‰**
15. $\frac{7}{10}$ **700‰**

16. $\frac{1}{2}$ **500‰**
17. $\frac{3}{4}$ **750‰**
18. $\frac{5}{8}$ **625‰**

19. $\frac{4}{5}$ **800‰**
20. $\frac{17}{20}$ **850‰**
21. $\frac{1}{3}$ **$333\frac{1}{3}$‰**

22. **CHALLENGE** In the United States, you will sometimes find the **mill** used as a monetary unit. What amount of money do you think is represented by 1 mill? **$0.001**

Enrichment Worksheet 10-7

Estimating Sales Tax

Many states charge a **sales tax** on purchases. To be sure that you have enough money, you should be able to estimate the amount of sales tax and the total cost of an item. For example, this is how you can estimate the total cost of the purchase shown at the right.

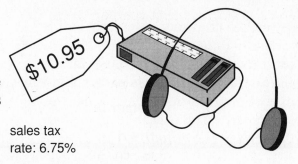

sales tax
rate: 6.75%

First, round the
price and the rate.
$10.95 → $11
6.75% → 7%

Multiply the rounded numbers.
11 dollars
× 7¢ per dollar
77¢ ≈ 80¢

7% means 7¢ per 100¢,
or 7¢ per dollar.

So, the total cost is close to $11 + 80¢, or $11.80.

Estimate the total cost of each purchase.

1. $6.98
sales tax
rate: 5%

2. $11.97
sales tax
rate: 5.75%

3. $19.88
sales tax
rate: 4.255%

4. $29.95
sales tax
rate: $6\frac{1}{2}$%

5. $79.00
sales tax
rate: $8\frac{1}{4}$%

6. $117.99
sales tax
rate: 6.25%

Will $50 be enough money to make each purchase?

7. $48.95
sales tax
rate: 3%

8. $46.99
sales tax
rate: 4.75%

9. $46.99
sales tax
rate: $8\frac{1}{4}$%

10. **CHALLENGE**   The price marked on a cassette tape is $8.99. With the sales tax, the total cost of the tape is $9.37. Estimate the sales tax rate.

Enrichment Worksheet 10-7

Estimating Sales Tax

Many states charge a **sales tax** on purchases. To be sure that you have enough money, you should be able to estimate the amount of sales tax and the total cost of an item. For example, this is how you can estimate the total cost of the purchase shown at the right.

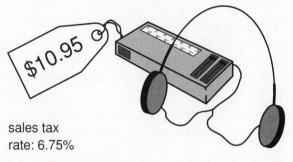

$10.95

sales tax
rate: 6.75%

First, round the price and the rate.
$10.95 → $11
6.75% → 7%

Multiply the rounded numbers.
11 dollars
× 7¢ per dollar
77¢ ≈ 80¢

7% means 7¢ per 100¢, or 7¢ per dollar.

So, the total cost is close to $11 + 80¢, or $11.80.

Estimate the total cost of each purchase.   **Estimates may vary.**

1. $6.98
sales tax
rate: 5%   **$7.35**

2. $11.97
sales tax
rate: 5.75%   **$12.72**

3. $19.88
sales tax
rate: 4.255%   **$20.80**

4. $29.95
sales tax
rate: $6\frac{1}{2}$%   **$32.10**

5. $79.00
sales tax
rate: $8\frac{1}{4}$%   **$86.40**

6. $117.99
sales tax
rate: 6.25%   **$127.20**

Will $50 be enough money to make each purchase?

7. $48.95
sales tax
rate: 3%   **no**

8. $46.99
sales tax
rate: 4.75%   **yes**

9. $46.99
sales tax
rate: $8\frac{1}{4}$%   **no**

10. **CHALLENGE**   The price marked on a cassette tape is $8.99. With the sales tax, the total cost of the tape is $9.37. Estimate the sales tax rate.   **a little more than 4%**

Enrichment Worksheet 10-8

Using 100%, 10%, and 1%

Many people think of 100%, 10%, and 1% as *key percents*.

100% is the **whole**.	100% of 24 = 1 × 24, or 24.
10% is **one tenth** of the whole.	10% of 24 = 0.1 × 24, or 2.4.
1% is **one hundredth** of the whole.	1% of 24 = 0.01 × 24, or 0.24.

Find the percent of each number.

1. 100% of 8,000　　　　　**2.** 10% of 8,000　　　　　**3.** 1% of 8,000

4. 10% of 640　　　　　**5.** 100% of 720　　　　　**6.** 1% of 290

7. 1% of 50　　　　　**8.** 100% of 33　　　　　**9.** 10% of 14

10. 100% of 2　　　　　**11.** 1% of 9　　　　　**12.** 10% of 7

This is how you can use the key percents to make some computations easier.

3% of 610 = __?__.	5% of 24 = __?__.
1% of 610 = 6.1,	10% of 24 = 2.4,
so 3% of 610 = 3 × 6.1, or 18.3.	so 5% of 24 = $\frac{1}{2}$ of 2.4, or 1.2.

Find the percent of each number.

13. 2% of 140　　　　　**14.** 8% of 2,100　　　　　**15.** 4% of 9

16. 20% of 233　　　　　**17.** 70% of 90　　　　　**18.** 30% of 4,110

19. 5% of 160　　　　　**20.** 5% of 38　　　　　**21.** 50% of 612

22. 25% of 168　　　　　**23.** 2.5% of 320　　　　　**24.** 2.5% of 28

Glencoe Division, Macmillan/McGraw-Hill

Enrichment Worksheet 10-8

Using 100%, 10%, and 1%

Many people think of 100%, 10%, and 1% as *key percents*.

100% is the **whole**.	100% of 24 = 1 × 24, or 24.
10% is **one tenth** of the whole.	10% of 24 = 0.1 × 24, or 2.4.
1% is **one hundredth** of the whole.	1% of 24 = 0.01 × 24, or 0.24.

Find the percent of each number.

1. 100% of 8,000   **8,000**   2. 10% of 8,000   **800**   3. 1% of 8,000   **80**

4. 10% of 640   **64**   5. 100% of 720   **720**   6. 1% of 290   **2.9**

7. 1% of 50   **0.5**   8. 100% of 33   **33**   9. 10% of 14   **1.4**

10. 100% of 2   **2**   11. 1% of 9   **0.09**   12. 10% of 7   **0.7**

This is how you can use the key percents to make some computations easier.

3% of 610 = __?__.	5% of 24 = __?__.
1% of 610 = 6.1,	10% of 24 = 2.4,
so 3% of 610 = 3 × 6.1, or 18.3.	so 5% of 24 = $\frac{1}{2}$ of 2.4, or 1.2.

Find the percent of each number.

13. 2% of 140   **2.8**   14. 8% of 2,100   **168**   15. 4% of 9   **0.36**

16. 20% of 233   **46.6**   17. 70% of 90   **63**   18. 30% of 4,110   **1,233**

19. 5% of 160   **8**   20. 5% of 38   **1.9**   21. 50% of 612   **306**

22. 25% of 168   **42**   23. 2.5% of 320   **8**   24. 2.5% of 28   **0.7**

Enrichment Worksheet 11-1

You Can Count on It!

How many triangles are there in the figure at the right?
How many parallelograms?

When counting shapes in a figure like this, you usually
have to think of different sizes.

 There are four
small triangles.

 There is one
large triangle. → There are five
triangles in all.

You also have to think of different positions.

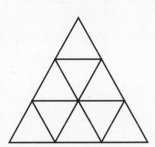 → There are three
parallelograms in all.

1. Now it's your turn. How many triangles are in the figure
   below? How many parallelograms? Use the space at the right
   to organize your counting.

2. A trapezoid is a quadrilateral with only one pair of sides
   parallel, as shown at the right. How many trapezoids are in
   the figure in Exercise 1?

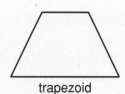

trapezoid

3. **CHALLENGE**   How many triangles, parallelograms,
   and trapezoids are in the figure at the right?

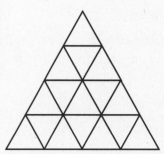

Enrichment Worksheet 11-1

You Can Count on It!

How many triangles are there in the figure at the right?
How many parallelograms?

When counting shapes in a figure like this, you usually
have to think of different sizes.

 There are four
small triangles.

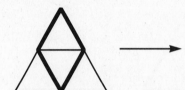 There is one
large triangle. —→ There are five
triangles in all.

You also have to think of different positions.

   ————————→ There are three
parallelograms in all.

1. Now it's your turn. How many triangles are in the figure
    below? How many parallelograms? Use the space at the right
    to organize your counting.

△ 9   ▱ 9

△ 3   ▱▱ + 6
                     ————
△ + 1   15 parallelograms
    ————
13 triangles

2. A trapezoid is a quadrilateral with only one pair of sides
    parallel, as shown at the right. How many trapezoids are in
    the figure in Exercise 1?   **18 trapezoids**

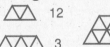 12

◁▷ 3   △ 3

trapezoid

3. *CHALLENGE*   How many triangles, parallelograms,
    and trapezoids are in the figure at the right?
    27 triangles
    45 parallelograms
    57 trapezoids

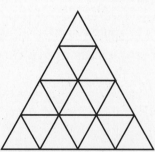

Enrichment Worksheet 11-2

Area of Composite Figures

A **composite figure** is made up, or composed, of other figures. For example, the L-shaped figure at the right is composed of two rectangles. To find the area of the L-shape, find the area of each rectangle, then add.

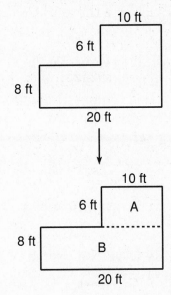

Area of A   Area of B

$A = l \times w$ $A = l \times w$

$A = 10 \times 6$ $A = 20 \times 8$

$A = 60$ $A = 160$

So, the area of the L-shaped figure is 60 ft² + 160 ft², or 220 ft².

Find the area of each composite figure.

1.

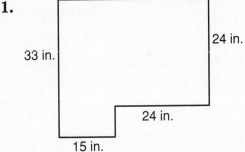

2.

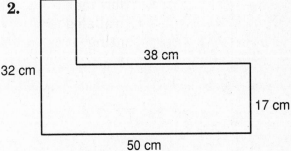

3.

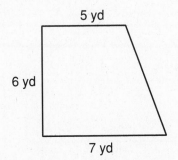

4.

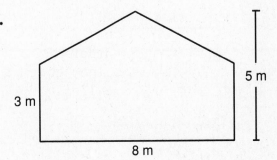

5. **CHALLENGE** Find the area of the shaded region in the figure at the right.

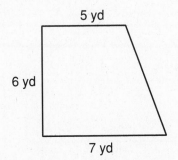

Enrichment Worksheet 11-2

Area of Composite Figures

A **composite figure** is made up, or composed, of other figures. For example, the L-shaped figure at the right is composed of two rectangles. To find the area of the L-shape, find the area of each rectangle, then add.

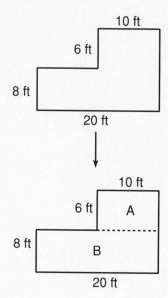

Area of A   Area of B

$A = l \times w$ $A = l \times w$

$A = 10 \times 6$ $A = 20 \times 8$

$A = 60$ $A = 160$

So, the area of the L-shaped figure is $60 \text{ ft}^2 + 160 \text{ ft}^2$, or 220 ft^2.

Find the area of each composite figure.

1.

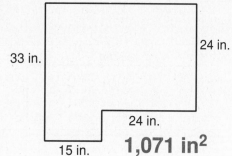

1,071 in²

2.   **1,030 cm²**

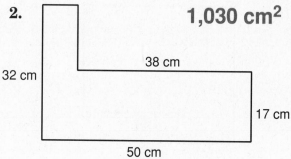

3.

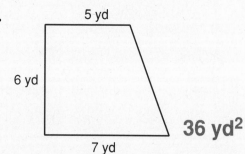

36 yd²

4.

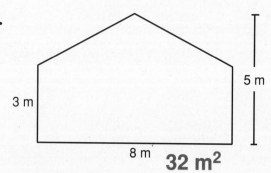

32 m²

5. **CHALLENGE** Find the area of the shaded region in the figure at the right. **367½ in²**

Enrichment Worksheet 11-3

Area of Sectors

In the circle at the right, the vertex of $\angle AOB$ is the center of the cirlce, So, $\angle AOB$ is called a **central angle** of the circle, and the shaded region is a **sector** of the circle. When you know the radius of the circle and the measure of the central angle, it's easy to find the area of the sector.

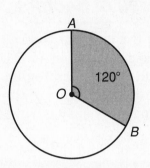

First find the area of the circle.

$A = \pi r^2$
$A \approx 3.14 \cdot (3)^2$
$A \approx 3.14 \cdot 9$
$A \approx 28.26$

Then find what fractional part of the circle is in the sector.

degree measure of central angle   ➔ $\dfrac{120}{360} = \dfrac{1}{3}$
degree measure of circle   ➔

So, the area of the sector is $\frac{1}{3}$ of 28.26 ft^2, or 9.42 ft^2.

Find the area of each shaded sector. Use 3.14 for π.

1.
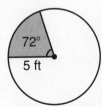

2.
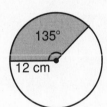

3.
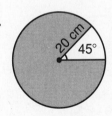

4.
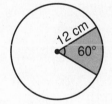

5.
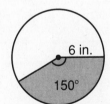

6.
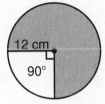

7. **CHALLENGE** In the circle at the right, the shaded region is called a **segment** of the circle. Find the area of the segment.

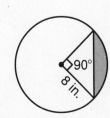

Enrichment Worksheet 11-3

Area of Sectors

In the circle at the right, the vertex of ∠AOB is the center of the cirlce, So, ∠AOB is called a **central angle** of the circle, and the shaded region is a **sector** of the circle. When you know the radius of the circle and the measure of the central angle, it's easy to find the area of the sector.

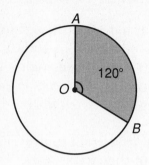

First find the area of the circle.

$A = \pi r^2$
$A \approx 3.14 \cdot (3)^2$
$A \approx 3.14 \cdot 9$
$A \approx 28.26$

Then find what fractional part of the circle is in the sector.

degree measure of central angle → $\frac{120}{360} = \frac{1}{3}$
degree measure of circle

So, the area of the sector is $\frac{1}{3}$ of 28.26 ft², or 9.42 ft².

Find the area of each shaded sector. Use 3.14 for π.

1.

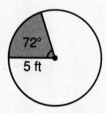

75.36 cm²

2.

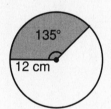

169.56 cm²

3.

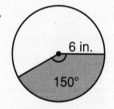

339.12 cm²

4.

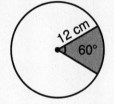

15.7 ft²

5.

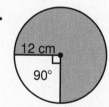

47.1 in²

6.

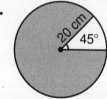

1,099 cm²

7. CHALLENGE In the circle at the right, the shaded region is called a **segment** of the circle. Find the area of the segment.   **18.24 in²**

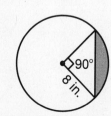

Enrichment Worksheet 11-4

Point of View

At the right is a square pyramid as seen from a point of
view that is slightly above and to the right. Here is the same
pyramid when you look at it from three different points
of view.

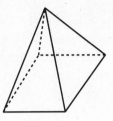

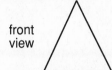 front
view

 side
view

 top
view

Notice that these views appear two-dimensional. Architects,
engineers, and designers often use views like these to
provide a detailed description of a three-dimensional object.

Identify the figure that each set of views represents.

1. front view 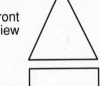   side view   top view

2. front view 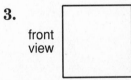   side view 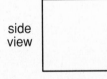   top view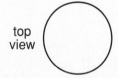

3. front view 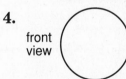   side view 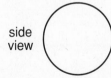   top view

4. front view   side view   top view

5. This figure is called a
truncated cone. In the
space at the right, sketch
front, side, and top views
of the figure.

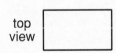

6. CHALLENGE At the right, you see
three different views of the same
cube. What symbol is on the face
opposite the plus sign?

Enrichment Worksheet 11-4

Point of View

At the right is a square pyramid as seen from a point of view that is slightly above and to the right. Here is the same pyramid when you look at it from three different points of view.

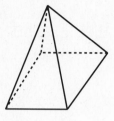

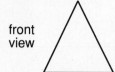 front view

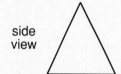 side view

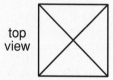 top view

Notice that these views appear two-dimensional. Architects, engineers, and designers often use views like these to provide a detailed description of a three-dimensional object.

Identify the figure that each set of views represents.

1.
front view   side view   top view    **cone**

2.
front view   side view   top view    **rectangular prism**

3.
front view   side view   top view   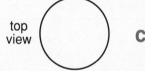 **cylinder**

4.
front view   side view   top view   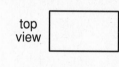 **sphere**

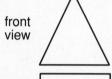

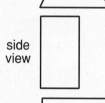
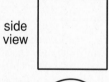
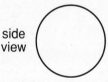

5. This figure is called a *truncated cone*. In the space at the right, sketch front, side, and top views of the figure.

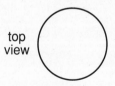

front   side   top

6. **CHALLENGE** At the right, you see three different views of the same cube. What symbol is on the face opposite the plus sign?   **$**

Glencoe Division, Macmillan/McGraw-Hill

Nets

A **net** is a two-dimensional pattern that can be folded to form a three-dimensional figure. For example, the figure at the right is a net for a rectangular prism.

Identify the figure that would be formed by folding each net.

1. 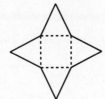   **2.**    **3.**   **4.**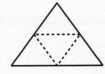

A **cube** is a rectangular prism in which all the edges have the same length. A net for a cube is made up of six squares. However, not every pattern of six squares is a net for a cube. For example, it would be impossible to fold the pattern at the right to form a cube.

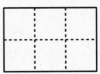

Tell whether each of these patterns is a net for a cube.

5. 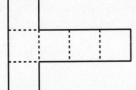   **6.** 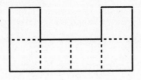   **7.**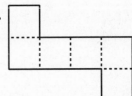

8. 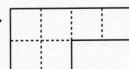   **9.** 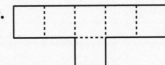   **10.**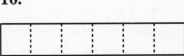

11. **CHALLENGE** In all, there are eleven different patterns of six squares that form a net for a cube. Sketch the eleven patterns in the space below.

Enrichment Worksheet 11-5

Nets

A **net** is a two-dimensional pattern that can be folded to form a three-dimensional figure. For example, the figure at the right is a net for a rectangular prism.

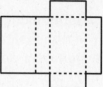

Identify the figure that would be formed by folding each net.

1.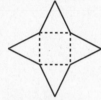

square pyramid

2.

cone

3.

cylinder

4.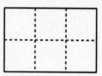

triangular pyramid

A **cube** is a rectangular prism in which all the edges have the same length. A net for a cube is made up of six squares. However, not every pattern of six squares is a net for a cube. For example, it would be impossible to fold the pattern at the right to form a cube.

Tell whether each of these patterns is a net for a cube.

5.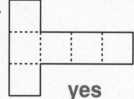

yes

6.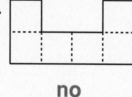

no

7.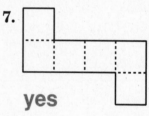

yes

8.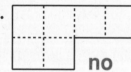

no

9.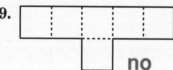

no

10.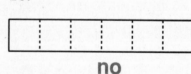

no

11. **CHALLENGE** In all, there are eleven different patterns of six squares that form a net for a cube. Sketch the eleven patterns in the space below.

Enrichment Worksheet 11-6

Volume and Liquid Capacity

The volume of a three-dimensional figure is the amount of *space* it contains. Volume is usually measured in cubic units—cubic meters, cubic inches, and so on.

The liquid capacity of a container is the amount of *liquid* it can hold. Liquid capacity generally is measured in units like liters, milliliters, cups, pints, quarts, and gallons.

The chart at the right shows the relationship between volume and liquid capacity. If a container were shaped like the rectangular prism below the chart, this is how you would find its liquid capacity.

> **Volume and Liquid Capacity**
>
> Metric
> $$1 \text{ cm}^3 = 1 \text{ mL}$$
> $$1 \text{ m}^3 = 1,000 \text{L}$$
>
> Customary
> $$1 \text{ in}^3 = 0.544 \text{ fl oz}$$
> $$1 \text{ ft}^3 = 7.481 \text{ gal}$$

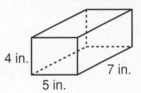

4 in.   5 in.   7 in.

Volume	Liquid Capacity
$V = lwh$	$1 \text{ in}^3 \approx 0.544 \text{ fl oz}$
$V = 7 \times 5 \times 4$	$140 \text{ in}^3 \approx (140 \times 0.544) \text{ fl oz}$
$V = 140$	$140 \text{ in}^3 \approx 76.16 \text{ fl oz}$

So, the liquid capacity of the container is about 76 fluid ounces.

Find the liquid capacity of a container shaped like a rectangular prism with the given dimensions. If necessary, round to the nearest whole number.

1. length, 8 cm
   width, 4 cm
   height, 6 cm

2. length, 7 ft
   width, 2 ft
   height, 3 ft

3. length, 3.5 m
   width, 1.5 m
   height, 5 m

4. length, 5 in.
   width, $1\frac{1}{2}$ in.
   height, $3\frac{1}{2}$ in.

5. An aquarium is 36 inches long, 18 inches wide, and 18 inches tall. It is filled with water to a height of 12 inches. How many gallons of water are in the aquarium? (Round to the nearest gallon.)

6. **CHALLENGE** How many cubic inches of space are occupied by one quart of water?

Enrichment Worksheet 11-6

Volume and Liquid Capacity

The volume of a three-dimensional figure is the amount of *space* it contains. Volume is usually measured in cubic units—cubic meters, cubic inches, and so on.

The liquid capacity of a container is the amount of *liquid* it can hold. Liquid capacity generally is measured in units like liters, milliliters, cups, pints, quarts, and gallons.

The chart at the right shows the relationship between volume and liquid capacity. If a container were shaped like the rectangular prism below the chart, this is how you would find its liquid capacity.

Volume and Liquid Capacity
Metric
$1 \text{ cm}^3 = 1 \text{ mL}$
$1 \text{ m}^3 = 1{,}000 \text{L}$
Customary
$1 \text{ in}^3 = 0.544 \text{ fl oz}$
$1 \text{ ft}^3 = 7.481 \text{ gal}$

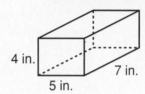

4 in.   5 in.   7 in.

Volume	Liquid Capacity
$V = lwh$	$1 \text{ in}^3 \approx 0.544 \text{ fl oz}$
$V = 7 \times 5 \times 4$	$140 \text{ in}^3 \approx (140 \times 0.544) \text{ fl oz}$
$V = 140$	$140 \text{ in}^3 \approx 76.16 \text{ fl oz}$

So, the liquid capacity of the container is about 76 fluid ounces.

Find the liquid capacity of a container shaped like a rectangular prism with the given dimensions. If necessary, round to the nearest whole number.

1. length, 8 cm
   width, 4 cm
   height, 6 cm **192 mL**

2. length, 7 ft
   width, 2 ft
   height, 3 ft **314 gal**

3. length, 3.5 m
   width, 1.5 m
   height, 5 m **26,250 L**

4. length, 5 in.
   width, $1\frac{1}{2}$ in.
   height, $3\frac{1}{2}$ in. **14 fl oz**

5. An aquarium is 36 inches long, 18 inches wide, and 18 inches tall. It is filled with water to a height of 12 inches. How many gallons of water are in the aquarium? (Round to the nearest gallon.) **34 gallons**

6. **CHALLENGE** How many cubic inches of space are occupied by one quart of water? **about 59 cubic inches**

Enrichment Worksheet 11-7

Modeling with Cubes

Some three-dimensional figures have
irregular shapes, like the one shown at the
right. When a problem involves a figure like
this, you may find it helpful to model the
figure using small cubes.

Volume =
3 cubic units

Surface Area =
14 square units

Find the volume and surface area of each figure.

1.

Volume =

Surface Area =

2.

Volume =

Surface Area =

3.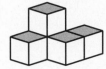

Volume =

Surface Area =

4.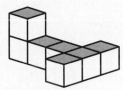

Volume =

Surface Area =

5.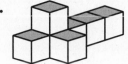

Volume =

Surface Area =

6.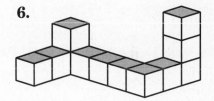

Volume =

Surface Area =

7. *CHALLENGE* There are five
different three-dimensional figures
that can be formed using four cubes.
The volume of each figure, of course,
is four cubic units. In the space at
the right, sketch the one that has
the least surface area.

Enrichment Worksheet 11-7

Modeling with Cubes

Some three-dimensional figures have irregular shapes, like the one shown at the right. When a problem involves a figure like this, you may find it helpful to model the figure using small cubes.

Volume =
3 cubic units

Surface Area =
14 square units

Find the volume and surface area of each figure.

1.

Volume =
4 cubic units

Surface Area =
18 square units

2.

Volume =
4 cubic units

Surface Area =
18 square units

3.

Volume =
5 cubic units

Surface Area =
22 square units

4.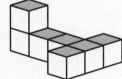

Volume =
7 cubic units

Surface Area =
30 square units

5.

Volume =
7 cubic units

Surface Area =
30 square units

6.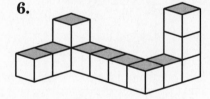

Volume =
12 cubic units

Surface Area =
50 square units

7. CHALLENGE There are five different three-dimensional figures that can be formed using four cubes. The volume of each figure, of course, is four cubic units. In the space at the right, sketch the one that has the least surface area.

Enrichment Worksheet 12-1

Graphs with Integers

Statistical graphs that display temperatures, elevations, and similar data often involve negative quantities. On graphs like these, the scale usually will have a zero point and will include both positive and negative numbers.

Use the bar graph at the right to answer each question.

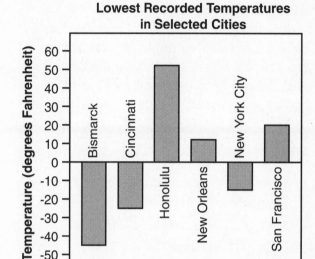

Lowest Recorded Temperatures in Selected Cities

1. In which cities is the record low temperature greater than 0°F?

2. In which cities is the record low temperature less than 0°F?

3. In which city is the record low temperature about −25°F?

4. Estimate the record low temperature for New York City.

5. In which cities is the record low temperature less than twenty degrees from 0°F?

6. How many degrees are between the record low temperatures for Bismarck and Honolulu?

7. In the space at the right, make a bar graph for these data.

Altitudes of Some California Locations Relative to Sea Level

Location	Altitude in Feet
Alameda	30
Brawley	−112
Calexico	7
Death Valley	−282
El Centro	−39
Salton City	−230

Enrichment Worksheet 12-1

Graphs with Integers

Statistical graphs that display temperatures, elevations, and similar data often involve negative quantities. On graphs like these, the scale usually will have a zero point and will include both positive and negative numbers.

Lowest Recorded Temperatures in Selected Cities

Use the bar graph at the right to answer each question.

1. In which cities is the record low temperature greater than 0°F?
   ## Honolulu, New Orleans, San Francisco

2. In which cities is the record low temperature less than 0°F?
   ## Bismark, Cincinnati, New York City

3. In which city is the record low temperature about −25°F?
   ## Cincinnati

4. Estimate the record low temperature for New York City.
   ## about −15°F

5. In which cities is the record low temperature less than twenty degrees from 0°F?
   ## New Orleans, New York City

6. How many degrees are between the record low temperatures for Bismarck and Honolulu?
   ## about 100°F

7. In the space at the right, make a bar graph for these data.

Altitudes of Some California Locations Relative to Sea Level

Location	Altitude in Feet
Alameda	30
Brawley	−112
Calexico	7
Death Valley	−282
El Centro	−39
Salton City	−230

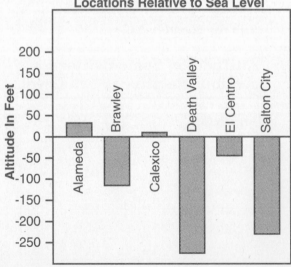

Altitudes of Some California Locations Relative to Sea Level

Enrichment Worksheet 12-2

Percent of Change

Positive and negative percents are often used to describe how a quantity has changed. Here are two examples.

original salary: $200
new salary: $250

original weight: 200 pounds
new weight: 180 pounds

amount of change: 250 − 200 = 50

amount of change: 200 − 180 = 20

percent of change: $\frac{50}{200} = \frac{25}{100} = 25\%$

percent of change: $\frac{20}{200} = \frac{10}{100} = 10\%$

Since the change was an *increase*, the percent of change is +25%.

Since the change was a *decrease*, the percent of change is −10%.

Find each percent of change.

1. original price: $50
new price: $25

2. original height: 50 inches
new height: 60 inches

3. original weight: 200 pounds
new weight: 190 pounds

4. original distance: 200 meters
new distance: 350 meters

5. original cost: $400
new cost: $480

6. original length: 25 inches
new length: 16 inches

7. *CHALLENGE* Complete the table.

Enrollment at King Middle School			
	Grade 6	**Grade 7**	**Grade 8**
Last year	240	270	240
This year	216	243	276
Percent of change			

8. Refer to the data in Exercise 7. What is the percent of change for the total enrollment of King Middle School?

Enrichment Worksheet 12-2

Percent of Change

Positive and negative percents are often used to describe how a quantity has changed. Here are two examples.

original salary: $200
new salary: $250

amount of change: $250 - 200 = 50$
percent of change: $\frac{50}{200} = \frac{25}{100} = 25\%$

Since the change was an *increase*, the percent of change is $+25\%$.

original weight: 200 pounds
new weight: 180 pounds

amount of change: $200 - 180 = 20$
percent of change: $\frac{20}{200} = \frac{10}{100} = 10\%$

Since the change was a *decrease*, the percent of change is -10%.

Find each percent of change.

1. original price: $50
   new price: $25
   −50%

2. original height: 50 inches
   new height: 60 inches
   +20%

3. original weight: 200 pounds
   new weight: 190 pounds
   −5%

4. original distance: 200 meters
   new distance: 350 meters
   +75%

5. original cost: $400
   new cost: $480
   +20%

6. original length: 25 inches
   new length: 16 inches
   −36%

7. **CHALLENGE** Complete the table.

Enrollment at King Middle School			
	Grade 6	**Grade 7**	**Grade 8**
Last year	240	270	240
This year	216	243	276
Percent of change	**−10%**	**−10%**	**+15%**

8. Refer to the data in Exercise 7. What is the percent of change for the total enrollment of King Middle School? **+2%**

Enrichment Worksheet 12-3

Speedy Addition

How would you perform an addition like this?

$$-4 + 7 + (-1) + 4 + (-7) + (-5)$$

Some people add all the positive integers, add all the negative integers, then add the results.

$$-4 + (-1) + (-7) + (-5) = -17$$
$$7 + 4 = 11$$
$$\longrightarrow \quad -17 + 11 = -6$$

Other people find it easier to first group all the zero pairs.

$$\underbrace{-4 + 4}_{0} \;+\; \underbrace{7 + (-7)}_{0} \;+\; \underbrace{(-1) + (-5)}_{-6} \quad \longrightarrow \quad -6$$

Which method do you think you would prefer? Check it out by finding each of these sums.

1. $-9 + 5 + 3 + 9 + (-3)$

2. $-16 + 9 + (-11) + 16 + 11 + (-12) + (-9)$

3. $10 + (-8) + (-4) + (-2)$

4. $-6 + 14 + (-11) + (-8) + 7 + 11$

5. $-15 + 6 + (-12) + 3 + 9 + (-3)$

6. $20 + (-13) + (-5) + 13 + (-10) + 16 + (-5)$

7. $19 + (-7) + (-9) + (-9) + 15 + (-10) + 16$

8. $-4 + 17 + (-8) + 5 + (-17) + (-13) + 8 + (-12)$

9. $16 + (-11) + 4 + (-2) + 11 + (-14) + 5 + (-9)$

10. $-21 + 3 + (-7) + (-4) + (-8) + 15 + 6 + 12 + 15$

11. Which method(s) did you use in Exercises 1–10? Did you choose from the methods above, or did you use a different method? Explain.

Enrichment Worksheet 12-3

Speedy Addition

How would you perform an addition like this?

$$-4 + 7 + (-1) + 4 + (-7) + (-5)$$

Some people add all the positive integers, add all the negative integers, then add the results.

$$-4 + (-1) + (-7) + (-5) = -17$$
$$7 + 4 = 11$$
$$\longrightarrow \quad -17 + 11 = -6$$

Other people find it easier to first group all the zero pairs.

$$\underbrace{-4 + 4}_{0} \ + \ \underbrace{7 + (-7)}_{0} \ + \ \underbrace{(-1) + (-5)}_{-6} \quad \longrightarrow \quad -6$$

Which method do you think you would prefer? Check it out by finding each of these sums.

1. $-9 + 5 + 3 + 9 + (-3)$ **5**

2. $-16 + 9 + (-11) + 16 + 11 + (-12) + (-9)$ **−12**

3. $10 + (-8) + (-4) + (-2)$ **−4**

4. $-6 + 14 + (-11) + (-8) + 7 + 11$ **7**

5. $-15 + 6 + (-12) + 3 + 9 + (-3)$ **−12**

6. $20 + (-13) + (-5) + 13 + (-10) + 16 + (-5)$ **16**

7. $19 + (-7) + (-9) + (-9) + 15 + (-10) + 16$ **15**

8. $-4 + 17 + (-8) + 5 + (-17) + (-13) + 8 + (-12)$ **−24**

9. $16 + (-11) + 4 + (-2) + 11 + (-14) + 5 + (-9)$ **0**

10. $-21 + 3 + (-7) + (-4) + (-8) + 15 + 6 + 12 + 15$ **11**

11. Which method(s) did you use in Exercises 1–10? Did you choose from the methods above, or did you use a different method? Explain.   **Answers will vary.**

Enrichment Worksheet 12-4

Wind Chill Temperatures

When you go outside on a windy day, it usually *feels* much colder than the actual temperature on the thermometer. This happens because the wind causes you to lose more heat from the surface of your skin than you would lose if the air were still. The temperature you feel is called the **wind chill temperature.** The table below lists some of the wind chill temperatures that have been calculated by the National Weather Service.

Wind Chill Temperatures (degrees Fahrenheit)

Wind Speed (miles per hour)	Actual Temperature								
	20	15	10	5	0	−5	−10	−15	−20
5	16	12	7	0	−5	−10	−15	−21	−26
10	3	−3	−9	−15	−22	−27	−34	−40	−46
15	−5	−11	−18	−25	−31	−38	−45	−51	−58
20	−10	−17	−24	−31	−39	−46	−53	−60	−67
25	−15	−22	−29	−36	−44	−51	−59	−66	−74
30	−18	−25	−33	−41	−49	−56	−64	−71	−79
35	−20	−27	−35	−43	−52	−58	−67	−74	−82
40	−21	−29	−37	−45	−53	−60	−69	−76	−84
45	−22	−30	−38	−46	−54	−62	−70	−78	−85

Wind speeds greater than 45 miles per hour have little additional chilling effect.

Use the table above to answer each question.

1. If the wind speed is 10 miles per hour and the actual temperature is 0°F, what is the wind chill temperature?

2. Suppose that the actual temperature is −5°F and the wind speed is 15 miles per hour. How much colder than −5°F does it feel?

Describe the change in the wind chill temperature.

3. The wind speed remains constant at 10 miles per hour, but the actual temperature rises from −5°F to 20°F.

4. The actual temperature remains constant at −10°F, but the wind speed increases from 5 miles per hour to 35 miles per hour.

Estimate the wind chill temperature in each situation.

5. The actual temperature is 8°F and the wind speed is 22 miles per hour.

6. The actual temperature is −10°F and the wind speed is 55 miles per hour.

Enrichment Worksheet 12-4

Wind Chill Temperatures

When you go outside on a windy day, it usually *feels* much colder than the actual temperature on the thermometer. This happens because the wind causes you to lose more heat from the surface of your skin than you would lose if the air were still. The temperature you feel is called the **wind chill temperature.** The table below lists some of the wind chill temperatures that have been calculated by the National Weather Service.

Wind Chill Temperatures (degrees Fahrenheit)

Wind Speed (miles per hour)	Actual Temperature								
	20	15	10	5	0	−5	−10	−15	−20
5	16	12	7	0	−5	−10	−15	−21	−26
10	3	−3	−9	−15	−22	−27	−34	−40	−46
15	−5	−11	−18	−25	−31	−38	−45	−51	−58
20	−10	−17	−24	−31	−39	−46	−53	−60	−67
25	−15	−22	−29	−36	−44	−51	−59	−66	−74
30	−18	−25	−33	−41	−49	−56	−64	−71	−79
35	−20	−27	−35	−43	−52	−58	−67	−74	−82
40	−21	−29	−37	−45	−53	−60	−69	−76	−84
45	−22	−30	−38	−46	−54	−62	−70	−78	−85

Wind speeds greater than 45 miles per hour have little additional chilling effect.

Use the table above to answer each question.

1. If the wind speed is 10 miles per hour and the actual temperature is 0°F, what is the wind chill temperature? **−22°F**

2. Suppose that the actual temperature is −5°F and the wind speed is 15 miles per hour. How much colder than −5°F does it feel?
33°F colder

Describe the change in the wind chill temperature.

3. The wind speed remains constant at 10 miles per hour, but the actual temperature rises from −5°F to 20°F.
rises 30°F

4. The actual temperature remains constant at −10°F, but the wind speed increases from 5 miles per hour to 35 miles per hour.
drops 52°F

Estimate the wind chill temperature in each situation.

5. The actual temperature is 8°F and the wind speed is 22 miles per hour.
Estimates will vary. Sample: about −30°F

6. The actual temperature is −10°F and the wind speed is 55 miles per hour. **about −70°F**

Enrichment Worksheet 12-5

Integer Patterns

Many number patterns involve integers. When you work with patterns like these, you need to pay special attention to the sign of each number in the pattern. Here are two examples.

1,   −2,   4,   −8,   16,   −32,   64, . . . ← *Multiply by −2.*
× (−2)   × (−2)   × (−2)   × (−2)   × (−2)   × (−2)

1,   3,   0,   2,   −1,   1,   −2, . . . ← *Add 2, subtract 3,*
+2   −3   +2   −3   +2   −3   *add 2, and so on.*

Write the next five numbers in each pattern shown above.

1. 1, −2, 4, −8, 16, −32, 64, _____, _____, _____, _____, _____

2. 1, 3, 0, 2, −1, 1, −2, _____, _____, _____, _____, _____

For each set of numbers, identify the pattern. Then write the next three numbers in the pattern.

3. −1, 3, −9, 27, −81, _____, _____, _____

4. 5, −1, −7, −13, −19, _____, _____, _____

5. −11, −8, −5, −2, 1, _____, _____, _____

6. −2, −10, −50, −250, −1,250, _____, _____, _____

7. 12, 7, 8, 3, 4, _____, _____, _____

8. −15, −10, −12, −7, −9, _____, _____, _____

9. 7, −7, −2, 2, 7, _____, _____, _____

10. 3, 6, −2, −4, −12, _____, _____, _____

11. −4, 8, 6, −12, −14, 28, _____, _____, _____

12. CHALLENGE 1, 2, 0, 3, −1, _____, _____, _____

Enrichment Worksheet 12-5

Integer Patterns

Many number patterns involve integers. When you work
with patterns like these, you need to pay special attention to
the sign of each number in the pattern. Here are two
examples.

1,   −2,   4,   −8,   16,   −32,   64, . . .   ← *Multiply by −2.*
× (−2) × (−2) × (−2) × (−2) × (−2) × (−2)

1,   3,   0,   2,   −1,   1,   −2, . . .← *Add 2, subtract 3,*
+2 −3 +2 −3 +2 −3   *add 2, and so on.*

Write the next five numbers in each pattern shown above.

1. 1, −2, 4, −8, 16, −32, 64, __−128__, __256__, __−512__, __1,024__, __−2,048__

2. 1, 3, 0, 2, −1, 1, −2, __0__, __−3__, __−1__, __−4__, __−2__

For each set of numbers, identify the pattern. Then write the
next three numbers in the pattern.

3. −1, 3, −9, 27, −81, __243__, __−729__, __2,187__   x −3

4. 5, −1, −7, −13, −19, __−25__, __−31__, __−37__   −6

5. −11, −8, −5, −2, 1, __4__, __7__, __10__   +3

6. −2, −10, −50, −250, −1,250, __−6,250__, __−31,250__, __−156,250__   x 5

7. 12, 7, 8, 3, 4, __−1__, __0__, __−5__   −5, +1

8. −15, −10, −12, −7, −9, __−4__, __−6__, __−1__   +5, −2

9. 7, −7, −2, 2, 7, __−7__, __−2__, __2__   −14, +5, +4, +5

10. 3, 6, −2, −4, −12, __−24__, __−32__, __−64__   x 2, −8

11. −4, 8, 6, −12, −14, 28, __26__, __−52__, __−54__   x −2, −2

12. CHALLENGE   1, 2, 0, 3, −1, __4__, __−2__, __5__   +1, −2, +3, −4

Glencoe Division, Macmillan/McGraw-Hill

Enrichment Worksheet 12-6

Integer Magic

A **magic triangle** is a triangular arrangement of numbers in which the sum of the numbers along each side is the same number. For example, in the magic triangle shown at the right, the sum of the numbers along each side is 0.

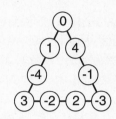

In each triangle, each of the integers from −4 to 4 appears exactly once. Complete the triangle so that the sum of the integers along each side is −3.

1.

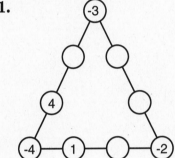

2.

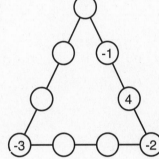

3.

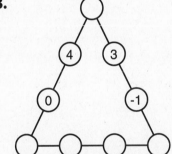

4.

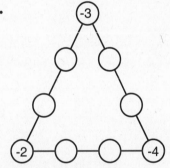

In these <u>magic stars</u>*, the sum of the integers along each line of the star is −2. Complete each magic star using the integers from −6 to 5 exactly once.*

5.

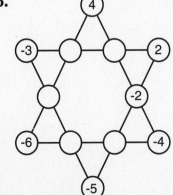

6.

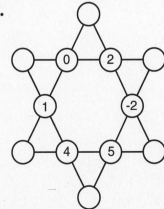

Integer Magic

A **magic triangle** is a triangular arrangement of numbers in which the sum of the numbers along each side is the same number. For example, in the magic triangle shown at the right, the sum of the numbers along each side is 0.

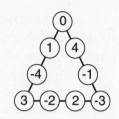
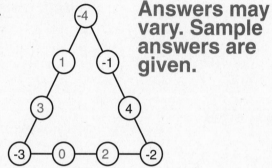

In each triangle, each of the integers from −4 to 4 appears exactly once. Complete the triangle so that the sum of the integers along each side is −3.

1.

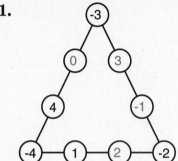

2.

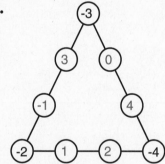

Answers may vary. Sample answers are given.

3.

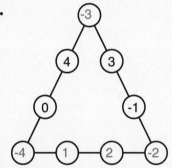

4.

(triangle)

In these __magic stars__, the sum of the integers along each line of the star is −2. Complete each magic star using the integers from −6 to 5 exactly once.

5.

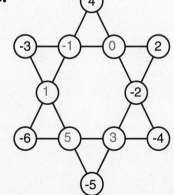

6.

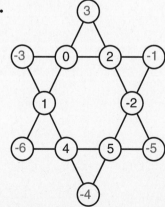

Enrichment Worksheet 12-7

Four Negative Fours

Do you think it is possible to use four negative fours to create an expression whose value is 1? Here are two ways to do it.

$$\frac{-4}{-4} + (-4) - (-4) = 1 + (-4) + 4 \quad \longleftarrow \quad \text{Remember that the}$$
$$= 1 \qquad \text{fraction bar is a}$$
$$\text{symbol for division}$$

$$\frac{-4 + (-4)}{-4 + (-4)} = \frac{-8}{-8} \text{ or } 1$$

On this page, you will be challenged to work backward. Instead of finding the value of a given expression, you will be asked to find an expression for a given value. In creating these expressions, you may use addition, subtraction, multiplication, and division in any combination—just be sure to follow the order of operations. You may also use parentheses and fraction bars to group numbers.

**Create an expression for each value by using
<u>two</u> negative fours.**

1. $0 =$ **2.** $1 =$

3. $16 =$ **4.** $-8 =$

**Create an expression for each value by using
<u>three</u> negative fours.**

5. $-3 =$ **6.** $5 =$

7. $2 =$ **8.** $-4 =$

9. $0 =$ **10.** $4 =$

**Create an expression for each value by using
<u>four</u> negative fours.**

11. $2 =$ **12.** $0 =$

13. $3 =$ **14.** $-2 =$

15. $-8 =$ **16.** $-5 =$

Enrichment Worksheet 12-7

Four Negative Fours

Do you think it is possible to use four negative fours to create an expression whose value is 1? Here are two ways to do it.

$$\frac{-4}{-4} + (-4) - (-4) = 1 + (-4) + 4 \longleftarrow \text{Remember that the fraction bar is a symbol for division}$$
$$= 1$$

$$\frac{-4 + (-4)}{-4 + (-4)} = \frac{-8}{-8} \text{ or } 1$$

On this page, you will be challenged to work backward. Instead of finding the value of a given expression, you will be asked to find an expression for a given value. In creating these expressions, you may use addition, subtraction, multiplication, and division in any combination—just be sure to follow the order of operations. You may also use parentheses and fraction bars to group numbers.

Create an expression for each value by using
two negative fours.

1. $0 = \quad -4 - (-4)$

2. $1 = \quad \frac{-4}{-4}$

3. $16 = \quad -4 \times (-4)$

4. $-8 = \quad -4 + (-4)$

Answers will vary. Sample answers are given.

Create an expression for each value by using
three negative fours.

5. $-3 = \quad \frac{-4}{-4} + (-4)$

6. $5 = \quad \frac{-4}{-4} - (-4)$

7. $2 = \quad \frac{-4 + (-4)}{-4}$

8. $-4 = \quad \frac{-4 \times (-4)}{-4}$

9. $0 = \quad \frac{-4 - (-4)}{-4}$

10. $4 = \quad -4 - (-4) - (-4)$

Create an expression for each value by using
four negative fours.

11. $2 = \quad \frac{-4}{-4} + \frac{-4}{-4}$

12. $0 = \quad \frac{-4}{-4} - \frac{-4}{-4}$

13. $3 = \quad \frac{-4 + (-4) + (-4)}{-4}$

14. $-2 = \quad \frac{-4 \times (-4)}{-4 + (-4)}$

15. $-8 = \quad \frac{-4}{-4} \times [-4 + (-4)]$

16. $-5 = \quad \frac{-4 \times (-4) - (-4)}{-4}$

Glencoe Division, Macmillan/McGraw-Hill

Enrichment Worksheet 12-8

Creative Coordinates

Graph each set of points on the coordinate grid below. Then use line segments to connect the points in the order given.

1. (−2, 5);   (1, 5);   (2, 6);   (1, 7);
(0, 7);   (−2, 5);   (−1, 8);   (−1, 9);
(−2, 9);   (−3, 8);   (−2, 5);   (−4, 7);
(−5, 7);   (−6, 6);   (−5, 5);   (−2, 5);
(−5, 4);   (−5, 3);   (−4, 2);   (−3, 2);
(−2, 5);   (−1, 2);   (0, 2);   (1, 3);
(1, 4);   (−2, 5);   (−2, −3); (0, 0);
(3, 1);   (−2, −3); (−1, −5); (−5, −4);
(−7, −5); (−1, −5); (3, −8)

2. (1, 6);   (−1, 6);   (−2, 8);
(−3, 6);   (−4, 5);   (−4, 2);
(−2, 0);   (−3, −1);   (−4, −3);
(−4, −6);   (−2, −8);   (7, −8);
(9, −7);   (11, −4);   (9, −5);
(7, −7);   (3, −7);   (4, −6);
(4, −3);   (3, −1);   (2, 0);
(4, 2);   (4, 5);   (3, 6);
(2, 8);   (1, 6)

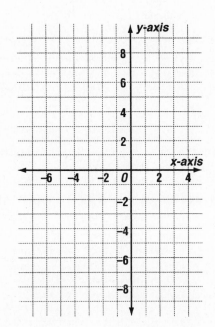

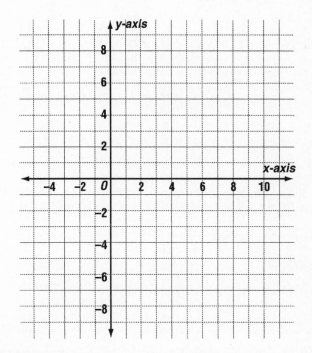

3. In the figure for Exercise 2, draw a line segment connecting each of the following pairs of points.
   a. (2, 2) and (5, 1)   **b.** (−2, 2) and (−5, 1)   **c.** (5, 3) and (2, 2)
   d. (−5, 3) and (−2, 2)   **e.** (2, 2) and (6, 2)   **f.** (−6, 2) and (−2, 2)

4. On a sheet of graph paper, create your own figure. Then record the coordinates of the points that form the figure.

Enrichment Worksheet 12-8

Creative Coordinates

Graph each set of points on the coordinate grid below. Then use line segments to connect the points in the order given.

1. $(-2, 5)$; $(1, 5)$; $(2, 6)$; $(1, 7)$;
$(0, 7)$; $(-2, 5)$; $(-1, 8)$; $(-1, 9)$;
$(-2, 9)$; $(-3, 8)$; $(-2, 5)$; $(-4, 7)$;
$(-5, 7)$; $(-6, 6)$; $(-5, 5)$; $(-2, 5)$;
$(-5, 4)$; $(-5, 3)$; $(-4, 2)$; $(-3, 2)$;
$(-2, 5)$; $(-1, 2)$; $(0, 2)$; $(1, 3)$;
$(1, 4)$; $(-2, 5)$; $(-2, -3)$; $(0, 0)$;
$(3, 1)$; $(-2, -3)$; $(-1, -5)$; $(-5, -4)$;
$(-7, -5)$; $(-1, -5)$; $(3, -8)$

2. $(1, 6)$; $(-1, 6)$; $(-2, 8)$;
$(-3, 6)$; $(-4, 5)$; $(-4, 2)$;
$(-2, 0)$; $(-3, -1)$; $(-4, -3)$;
$(-4, -6)$; $(-2, -8)$; $(7, -8)$;
$(9, -7)$; $(11, -4)$; $(9, -5)$;
$(7, -7)$; $(3, -7)$; $(4, -6)$;
$(4, -3)$; $(3, -1)$; $(2, 0)$;
$(4, 2)$; $(4, 5)$; $(3, 6)$;
$(2, 8)$; $(1, 6)$

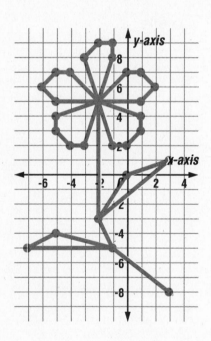

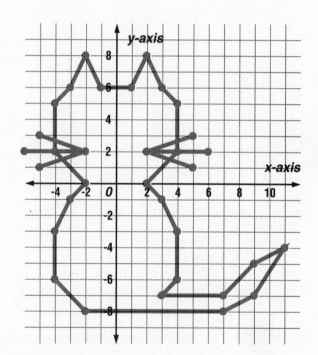

3. In the figure for Exercise 2, draw a line segment connecting each of the following pairs of points.
   a. $(2, 2)$ and $(5, 1)$ **b.** $(-2, 2)$ and $(-5, 1)$ **c.** $(5, 3)$ and $(2, 2)$
   d. $(-5, 3)$ and $(-2, 2)$ **e.** $(2, 2)$ and $(6, 2)$ **f.** $(-6, 2)$ and $(-2, 2)$

4. On a sheet of graph paper, create your own figure. Then record the coordinates of the points that form the figure.
   Answers will vary.

Enrichment Worksheet 12-9

Glide Reflections

A **glide reflection** is a transformation that is a combination of a reflection and a translation. In the figure at the right, △A′B′C′ is the image of △ABC under a glide reflection: △ABC was reflected across the *y*-axis, then translated 6 units down.

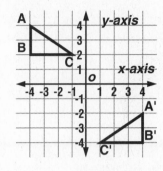

Draw the image of each figure under the given glide reflection.

1. reflection across the *x*-axis; translation 5 units left

2. reflection across the *y*-axis; translation 5 units up

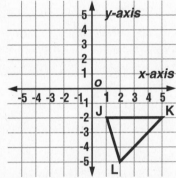

3. reflection across the *y*-axis; translation 2 units down

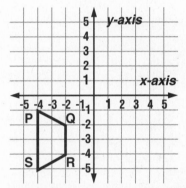

4. reflection across the *x*-axis; translation 6 units right

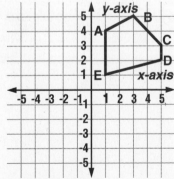

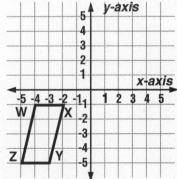

5. **CHALLENGE** A glide reflection is sometimes informally called a *walk*. Can you explain why? In the space at the right, draw a diagram to illustrate your answer.

Enrichment Worksheet 12-9

Glide Reflections

A **glide reflection** is a transformation that is a combination of a reflection and a translation. In the figure at the right, △A′B′C′ is the image of △ABC under a glide reflection: △ABC was reflected across the *y*-axis, then translated 6 units down.

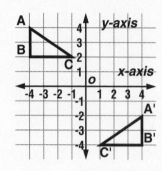

Draw the image of each figure under the given glide reflection.

1. reflection across the *x*-axis; translation 5 units left

2. reflection across the *y*-axis; translation 5 units up

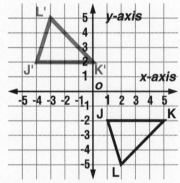

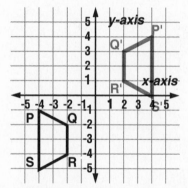

3. reflection across the *y*-axis; translation 2 units down

4. reflection across the *x*-axis; translation 6 units right

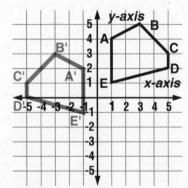

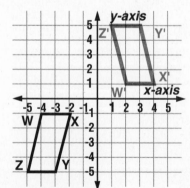

5. *CHALLENGE* A glide reflection is sometimes informally called a *walk*. Can you explain why? In the space at the right, draw a diagram to illustrate your answer.
It resembles a pattern of footprints.

Enrichment Worksheet 13-1

Clock Arithmetic

Did you realize that, when you work with elapsed time, you use a special kind of arithmetic that is called **clock arithmetic?** In clock arithmetic, you use the symbols $\oplus$ for addition and $\ominus$ for subtraction. Here are two examples.

8 o'clock plus 5 hours is 1 o'clock.

$$8 \oplus 5 = 1$$

4 o'clock minus 7 hours is 9 o'clock.

$$4 \ominus 7 = 9$$

Add or subtract using the 12-hour clock above.

1. $11 \oplus 3$ 2. $7 \oplus 9$ 3. $3 \ominus 10$ 4. $7 \ominus 8$

5. $2 \oplus 12$ 6. $2 \ominus 12$ 7. $4 \oplus 6$ 8. $9 \ominus 4$

To solve "clock equations" involving the 12-hour clock, use inverse operations.

$$d \oplus 5 = 2$$
$$d \oplus 5 \ominus 5 = 2 \ominus 5$$
$$d = 9$$

$$j \ominus 4 = 10$$
$$j \ominus 4 \oplus 4 = 10 \oplus 4$$
$$j = 2$$

Solve each equation using the 12-hour clock above.

9. $r \oplus 7 = 5$ 10. $x \ominus 9 = 11$ 11. $b \oplus 6 = 7$

12. $t \ominus 12 = 4$ 13. $n \ominus 4 = 3$ 14. $y \oplus 6 = 1$

CHALLENGE In clock arithmetic, you often work with clocks that have different numbers of hours. For example, the clock shown at the right is an *8-hour clock.*

Solve each equation using the 8-hour clock at the right.

15. $m \oplus 5 = 2$ 16. $z \ominus 4 = 7$ 17. $p \oplus 8 = 1$

18. $c \ominus 8 = 6$ 19. $w \ominus 4 = 8$ 20. $k \oplus 6 = 3$

Enrichment Worksheet 13-1

Clock Arithmetic

Did you realize that, when you work with elapsed time, you
use a special kind of arithmetic that is called **clock
arithmetic?** In clock arithmetic, you use the symbols $\oplus$ for
addition and $\ominus$ for subtraction. Here are two examples.

8 o'clock plus 5 hours is 1 o'clock.

$$8 \oplus 5 = 1$$

4 o'clock minus 7 hours is 9 o'clock.

$$4 \ominus 7 = 9$$

Add or subtract using the 12-hour clock above.

1. $11 \oplus 3$ **2**   2. $7 \oplus 9$ **4**   3. $3 \ominus 10$ **5**   4. $7 \ominus 8$ **11**

5. $2 \oplus 12$ **2**   6. $2 \ominus 12$ **2**   7. $4 \oplus 6$ **10**   8. $9 \ominus 4$ **5**

To solve "clock equations" involving the 12-hour clock, use
inverse operations.

$$d \oplus 5 = 2 \qquad\qquad j \ominus 4 = 10$$
$$d \oplus 5 \ominus 5 = 2 \ominus 5 \qquad j \ominus 4 \oplus 4 = 10 \oplus 4$$
$$d = 9 \qquad\qquad\qquad j = 2$$

Solve each equation using the 12-hour clock above.

9. $r \oplus 7 = 5$ **10**   10. $x \ominus 9 = 11$ **8**   11. $b \oplus 6 = 7$ **1**

12. $t \ominus 12 = 4$ **4**   13. $n \ominus 4 = 3$ **7**   14. $y \oplus 6 = 1$ **7**

CHALLENGE   In clock arithmetic, you often
work with clocks that have different numbers
of hours. For example, the clock shown at the
right is an *8-hour clock.*

Solve each equation using the 8-hour clock at the right.

15. $m \oplus 5 = 2$ **5**   16. $z \ominus 4 = 7$ **3**   17. $p \oplus 8 = 1$ **1**

18. $c \ominus 8 = 6$ **6**   19. $w \ominus 4 = 8$ **4**   20. $k \oplus 6 = 3$ **5**

Enrichment Worksheet 13-2

Patterns in Equations

On this page, you will explore patterns of change in equations.

For each table:
a. Describe how the equation changes from row to row.
b. Complete the Solution column.
c. Describe how the solution changes from row to row.

1.

Equation	Solution
$t + 3 = 4$	
$t + 3 = 3$	
$t + 3 = 2$	
$t + 3 = 1$	

2.

Equation	Solution
$3x = 6$	
$3x = 3$	
$3x = 0$	
$3x = -3$	

3.

Equation	Solution
$r - 3 = -2$	
$r - 3 = -1$	
$r - 3 = 0$	
$r - 3 = 1$	

4.

Equation	Solution
$m + 8 = 7$	
$m + 7 = 7$	
$m + 6 = 7$	
$m + 5 = 7$	

5.

Equation	Solution
$\frac{1}{5}j = 1$	
$\frac{1}{5}j = 0$	
$\frac{1}{5}j = -1$	
$\frac{1}{5}j = -2$	

6.

Equation	Solution
$\frac{1}{4}c = -1$	
$\frac{1}{3}c = -1$	
$\frac{1}{2}c = -1$	
$1c = -1$	

Glencoe Division, Macmillan/McGraw-Hill

Enrichment Worksheet 13-2

Patterns in Equations

On this page, you will explore patterns of change in equations.

For each table:
a. Describe how the equation changes from row to row.
b. Complete the Solution column.
c. Describe how the solution changes from row to row.

1.

Equation	Solution
$t + 3 = 4$	1
$t + 3 = 3$	0
$t + 3 = 2$	−1
$t + 3 = 1$	−2

a. Sum decreases by 1.
c. Solution decreases by 1.

2.

Equation	Solution
$3x = 6$	2
$3x = 3$	1
$3x = 0$	0
$3x = -3$	−1

a. Product decreases by 3.
c. Solution decreases by 1.

3.

Equation	Solution
$r - 3 = -2$	1
$r - 3 = -1$	2
$r - 3 = 0$	3
$r - 3 = 1$	4

a. Difference increases by 1.
c. Solution increases by 1.

4.

Equation	Solution
$m + 8 = 7$	−1
$m + 7 = 7$	0
$m + 6 = 7$	1
$m + 5 = 7$	2

a. Addend decreases by 1.
c. Solution increases by 1.

5.

Equation	Solution
$\frac{1}{5}j = 1$	5
$\frac{1}{5}j = 0$	0
$\frac{1}{5}j = -1$	−5
$\frac{1}{5}j = -2$	−10

a. Product decreases by 1.
c. Solution decreases by 5.

6.

Equation	Solution
$\frac{1}{4}c = -1$	−4
$\frac{1}{3}c = -1$	−3
$\frac{1}{2}c = -1$	−2
$1c = -1$	−1

a. Denominator decreases by 1.
c. Solution increases by 1.

Enrichment Worksheet 13-3

Equations as Models

When you write an equation that represents the information in a problem, the equation serves as a *model* for the problem. One equation can be a model for several different problems.

Each of Exercises 1-8 can be modeled by one of these equations:

$$n + 2 = 10 \qquad n - 2 = 10 \qquad 2n = 10 \qquad \frac{n}{2} = 10$$

Choose the correct equation. Then solve the problem.

1. Chum earned $10 for working two hours. How much did he earn per hour?

2. Ana needs $2 more to buy a $10 scarf. How much money does she already have?

3. Kathy and her brother won a contest and shared the prize equally. Each received $10. What was the amount of the prize?

4. Jameel loaned two tapes to a friend. He has ten tapes left. How many tapes did Jameel originally have?

5. In the figure below, the length of $\overline{AC}$ is 10 cm. The length of $\overline{BC}$ is 2 cm. What is the length of $\overline{AB}$?

6. Ray AC bisects $\angle BAD$. The measure of $\angle BAC$ is 10°. What is the measure of $\angle BAD$?

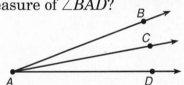

7. The width of the rectangle below is 2 inches less than the length. What is the length?

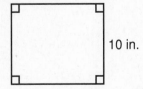

10 in.

8. In the triangle below, the length of $\overline{PQ}$ is twice the length of $\overline{QR}$. What is the length of $\overline{QR}$?

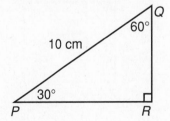

10 cm

9. CHALLENGE On a separate sheet of paper, write a problem that can be modeled by the equation $3a + 5 = 29$.

Enrichment Worksheet 13-3

Equations as Models

When you write an equation that represents the information in a problem, the equation serves as a *model* for the problem. One equation can be a model for several different problems.

Each of Exercises 1-8 can be modeled by one of these equations:

$$n + 2 = 10 \qquad n - 2 = 10 \qquad 2n = 10 \qquad \frac{n}{2} = 10$$

Choose the correct equation. Then solve the problem.

1. Chum earned $10 for working two hours. How much did he earn per hour? **$2n = 10$; $5**

2. Ana needs $2 more to buy a $10 scarf. How much money does she already have? **$n + 2 = 10$; $8**

3. Kathy and her brother won a contest and shared the prize equally. Each received $10. What was the amount of the prize? **$\frac{n}{2} = 10$; $20**

4. Jameel loaned two tapes to a friend. He has ten tapes left. How many tapes did Jameel originally have? **$n - 2 = 10$; 12 tapes**

5. In the figure below, the length of $\overline{AC}$ is 10 cm. The length of $\overline{BC}$ is 2 cm. What is the length of $\overline{AB}$?

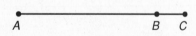

   $n + 2 = 10$; 8 cm

6. Ray AC bisects $\angle BAD$. The measure of $\angle BAC$ is 10°. What is the measure of $\angle BAD$?

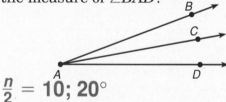

   $\frac{n}{2} = 10$; 20°

7. The width of the rectangle below is 2 inches less than the length. What is the length?

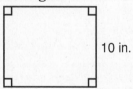

10 in.

   $n - 2 = 10$; 12 inches

8. In the triangle below, the length of $\overline{PQ}$ is twice the length of $\overline{QR}$. What is the length of $\overline{QR}$?

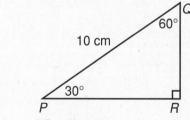

   $2n = 10$; 5 cm

9. **CHALLENGE** On a separate sheet of paper, write a problem that can be modeled by the equation $3a + 5 = 29$.
   Answers will vary.

Glencoe Division, Macmillan/McGraw-Hill

Enrichment Worksheet 13-4

Function Rules and Dot Patterns

Function rules are often used to describe geometric patterns. In the pattern at the right, for example, do you see this relationship?

1st figure: $3 \times 1 = 3$ dots

2nd figure: $3 \times 2 = 6$ dots

3rd figure: $3 \times 3 = 9$ dots

4th figure: $3 \times 4 = 12$ dots

So, the "*n*th" figure in this pattern would have $3 \times n$, or $3n$, dots. A function rule that describes the pattern is $3n$.

1st ••• ⟶ 3 dots

2nd ••• ⟶ 6 dots

3rd ••• ⟶ 9 dots

4th ••• ⟶ 12 dots

Write a function rule to describe each dot pattern.

1. 1st
2nd
3rd
4th

2. 1st
2nd
3rd
4th

3. 1st
2nd
3rd
4th

4. 1st
2nd
3rd
4th

5. 1st
2nd
3rd
4th

6. 1st
2nd
3rd
4th

7. *CHALLENGE* Create your own dot pattern. Then exchange patterns with a classmate. Try to find the function rule for each other's patterns.

Glencoe Division, Macmillan/McGraw-Hill

Enrichment Worksheet 13-4

Function Rules and Dot Patterns

Function rules are often used to describe geometric patterns. In the pattern at the right, for example, do you see this relationship?

1st figure: $3 \times 1 = 3$ dots

2nd figure: $3 \times 2 = 6$ dots

3rd figure: $3 \times 3 = 9$ dots

4th figure: $3 \times 4 = 12$ dots

So, the "*n*th" figure in this pattern would have $3 \times n$, or $3n$, dots. A function rule that describes the pattern is $3n$.

1st → 3 dots

2nd → 6 dots

3rd → 9 dots

4th → 12 dots

Write a function rule to describe each dot pattern.

1. 1st
2nd
3rd
4th $4n$

2. 1st
2nd
3rd
4th $n + 3$

3. 1st
2nd
3rd
4th $3n - 1$

4. 1st
2nd
3rd
4th n^2

5. 1st
2nd
3rd
4th $n^2 + 1$

6. 1st
2nd
3rd
4th $n^2 + n$
or
$n(n + 1)$

7. CHALLENGE Create your own dot pattern. Then exchange patterns with a classmate. Try to find the function rule for each other's patterns. **Answers will vary.**

Glencoe Division, Macmillan/McGraw-Hill

Enrichment Worksheet 13-5

Interpreting Graphs of Functions

An everyday example of a function is the relationship between distance and time. You can picture this relationship in a graph like the one at the right. This particular graph pictures a situation in which a person travels at a constant rate, and so the graph is a straight line segment.

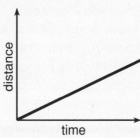

In reality, you seldom travel at a constant rate during an entire trip. You might switch from running to walking, for example, or you might stop to rest. On this page, you will work with graphs that represent situations like these.

Refer to the graphs below. Write the letter of the graph that best pictures each of these situations.

1. Patty ran for 15 minutes, then walked for 15 minutes.

2. Helmer walked for 15 minutes, then ran for 15 minutes.

3. Dale ran for 10 minutes, stopped to rest for 10 minutes, then walked for 10 minutes.

4. Josita ran for 10 minutes, stopped to rest for 10 minutes, then ran for 10 more minutes.

5. Janette ran for 10 minutes, walked for 10 minutes, then ran for 10 more minutes.

6. Ralph ran for 15 minutes, walked for 10 minutes, then ran for 5 more minutes.

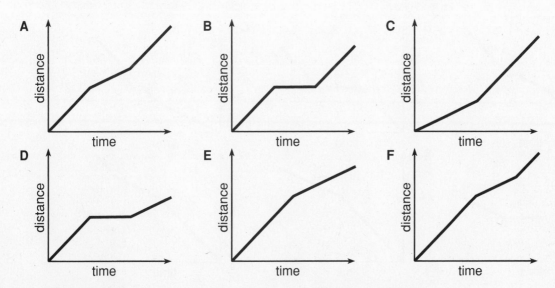

7. **CHALLENGE**   Assume that all the people described in Exercises 1 – 6 ran at the same rate, and they all walked at the same rate. Who traveled farthest in 30 minutes?

Glencoe Division, Macmillan/McGraw-Hill

Enrichment Worksheet 13-5

Interpreting Graphs of Functions

An everyday example of a function is the relationship between distance and time. You can picture this relationship in a graph like the one at the right. This particular graph pictures a situation in which a person travels at a constant rate, and so the graph is a straight line segment.

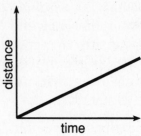

In reality, you seldom travel at a constant rate during an entire trip. You might switch from running to walking, for example, or you might stop to rest. On this page, you will work with graphs that represent situations like these.

Refer to the graphs below. Write the letter of the graph that best pictures each of these situations.

1. Patty ran for 15 minutes, then walked for 15 minutes. **E**

2. Helmer walked for 15 minutes, then ran for 15 minutes. **C**

3. Dale ran for 10 minutes, stopped to rest for 10 minutes, then walked for 10 minutes. **D**

4. Josita ran for 10 minutes, stopped to rest for 10 minutes, then ran for 10 more minutes. **B**

5. Janette ran for 10 minutes, walked for 10 minutes, then ran for 10 more minutes. **A**

6. Ralph ran for 15 minutes, walked for 10 minutes, then ran for 5 more minutes. **F**

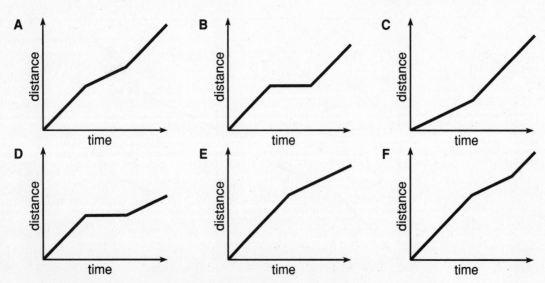

7. **CHALLENGE** Assume that all the people described in Exercises 1 – 6 ran at the same rate, and they all walked at the same rate. Who traveled farthest in 30 minutes?
   Janette and Ralph

Enrichment Worksheet 13-6

Compound Inequalities

Statements that consist of two or more inequalities are called **compound inequalities.** When you graph a compound inequality, you need to pay special attention to the words that connect the inequalities.

$t < 3$ or $t > 2$

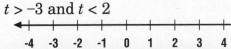

-4 -3 -2 -1 0 1 2 3 4

The graph includes all numbers that are *either* less than –3 or greater than 2.

$t > -3$ and $t < 2$

-4 -3 -2 -1 0 1 2 3 4

The graph includes all numbers that are *both* greater than –3 *and* less than 2.

Graph each compound inequality.

1. $h > -5$ and $h < 4$

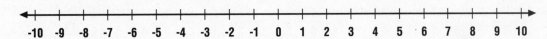

-10 -9 -8 -7 -6 -5 -4 -3 -2 -1 0 1 2 3 4 5 6 7 8 9 10

2. $q < -7$ or $q > 6$

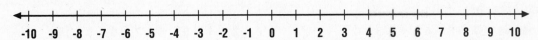

-10 -9 -8 -7 -6 -5 -4 -3 -2 -1 0 1 2 3 4 5 6 7 8 9 10

3. $x \geq 0$ and $x \leq 8$

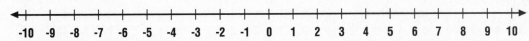

-10 -9 -8 -7 -6 -5 -4 -3 -2 -1 0 1 2 3 4 5 6 7 8 9 10

4. $k \geq 4$ or $k \leq -2$

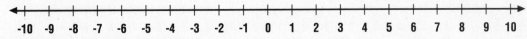

-10 -9 -8 -7 -6 -5 -4 -3 -2 -1 0 1 2 3 4 5 6 7 8 9 10

5. $r \leq -3$ or $r > 0$

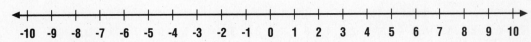

-10 -9 -8 -7 -6 -5 -4 -3 -2 -1 0 1 2 3 4 5 6 7 8 9 10

6. $a < 8$ and $a \geq -4$

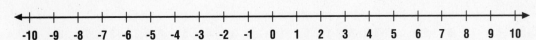

-10 -9 -8 -7 -6 -5 -4 -3 -2 -1 0 1 2 3 4 5 6 7 8 9 10

7. *CHALLENGE* Describe the graph of each inequality.

a. $m < -4$ and $m > 4$ **b.** $m > -4$ or $m < 4$

Enrichment Worksheet 13-6

Compound Inequalities

Statements that consist of two or more inequalities are called **compound inequalities.** When you graph a compound inequality, you need to pay special attention to the words that connect the inequalities.

$t < 3$ or $t > 2$

-4 -3 -2 -1 0 1 2 3 4

The graph includes all numbers that are *either* less than –3 *or* greater than 2.

$t > -3$ and $t < 2$

-4 -3 -2 -1 0 1 2 3 4

The graph includes all numbers that are *both* greater than –3 *and* less than 2.

Graph each compound inequality.

1. $h > -5$ and $h < 4$

2. $q < -7$ or $q > 6$

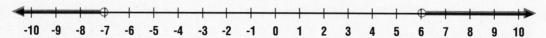

3. $x \geq 0$ and $x \leq 8$

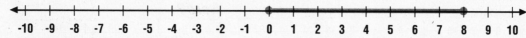

4. $k \geq 4$ or $k \leq -2$

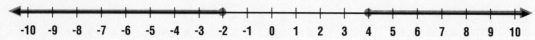

5. $r \leq -3$ or $r > 0$

6. $a < 8$ and $a \geq -4$

7. *CHALLENGE* Describe the graph of each inequality.

a. $m < -4$ and $m > 4$
number line with
no points graphed

b. $m > -4$ or $m < 4$
number line with
all points graphed

Enrichment Worksheet 14-1

Working Backward with Probabilities

Suppose that you are given this information about rolling a
number cube.

$$P(1) = \tfrac{1}{2} \qquad P(3) = \tfrac{1}{3} \qquad P(5) = \tfrac{1}{6}$$

Can you tell what numbers are marked on the faces of the
cube? Work backward. Since a cube has six faces, express
each probability as a fraction whose denominator is 6.

$$P(1) = \tfrac{3}{6} \qquad P(3) = \tfrac{2}{6} \qquad P(5) = \tfrac{1}{6}$$

So, the cube must have three faces marked with the number 1,
two faces marked 3, and one face marked 5.

Each set of probabilities is associated with rolling a number cube. What numbers are marked on the faces of the cube?

1. $P(2) = \tfrac{1}{3}$

$P(4) = \tfrac{1}{3}$

$P(6) = \tfrac{1}{3}$

2. $P(1) = \tfrac{1}{6}$

$P(4) = \tfrac{1}{6}$

$P(\text{factor of 4}) = 1$

3. $P(1 \text{ or } 2) = \tfrac{5}{6}$

$P(2 \text{ or } 3) = \tfrac{2}{3}$

$P(1, 2, \text{ or } 3) = 1$

Each set of probabilities is associated with the spinner shown at the right. How many sections of each color are there?

4. $P(\text{red}) = \tfrac{1}{2}$

$P(\text{blue}) = \tfrac{1}{4}$

$P(\text{green}) = \tfrac{1}{8}$

$P(\text{black}) = \tfrac{1}{8}$

5. $P(\text{yellow or purple}) = \tfrac{5}{8}$

$P(\text{purple or white}) = \tfrac{3}{4}$

$P(\text{green or blue}) = 0$

$P(\text{yellow, purple, or white}) = 1$

6. Suppose that you are given this information
about pulling a marble out of a bag.

$$P(\text{green}) = \tfrac{1}{4} \qquad P(\text{blue}) = \tfrac{1}{6} \qquad P(\text{red}) = \tfrac{3}{8}$$

$$P(\text{yellow}) = \tfrac{1}{24} \quad P(\text{white}) = \tfrac{1}{24} \quad P(\text{black}) = \tfrac{1}{8}$$

If the bag contains 48 marbles, how many marbles of
each color are there?

Enrichment Worksheet 14-1

Working Backward with Probabilities

Suppose that you are given this information about rolling a number cube.

$$P(1) = \tfrac{1}{2} \qquad P(3) = \tfrac{1}{3} \qquad P(5) = \tfrac{1}{6}$$

Can you tell what numbers are marked on the faces of the cube? Work backward. Since a cube has six faces, express each probability as a fraction whose denominator is 6.

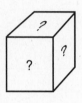

$$P(1) = \tfrac{3}{6} \qquad P(3) = \tfrac{2}{6} \qquad P(5) = \tfrac{1}{6}$$

So, the cube must have three faces marked with the number 1, two faces marked 3, and one face marked 5.

Each set of probabilities is associated with rolling a number cube. What numbers are marked on the faces of the cube?

1. $P(2) = \tfrac{1}{3}$

$P(4) = \tfrac{1}{3}$

$P(6) = \tfrac{1}{3}$

2, 2, 4, 4, 6, 6

2. $P(1) = \tfrac{1}{6}$

$P(4) = \tfrac{1}{6}$

$P(\text{factor of } 4) = 1$

1, 2, 2, 2, 2, 4

3. $P(1 \text{ or } 2) = \tfrac{5}{6}$

$P(2 \text{ or } 3) = \tfrac{2}{3}$

$P(1, 2, \text{ or } 3) = 1$

1, 1, 2, 2, 2, 3

Each set of probabilities is associated with the spinner shown at the right. How many sections of each color are there?

4. $P(\text{red}) = \tfrac{1}{2}$

$P(\text{blue}) = \tfrac{1}{4}$ **4 red**

$P(\text{green}) = \tfrac{1}{8}$ **2 blue**

$P(\text{black}) = \tfrac{1}{8}$ **1 green**
                     1 black

5. $P(\text{yellow or purple}) = \tfrac{5}{8}$

$P(\text{purple or white}) = \tfrac{3}{4}$

$P(\text{green or blue}) = 0$

$P(\text{yellow, purple, or white}) = 1$

2 yellow
3 purple
3 white
0 green
0 blue

6. Suppose that you are given this information about pulling a marble out of a bag.

$$P(\text{green}) = \tfrac{1}{4} \qquad P(\text{blue}) = \tfrac{1}{6} \qquad P(\text{red}) = \tfrac{3}{8}$$

$$P(\text{yellow}) = \tfrac{1}{24} \qquad P(\text{white}) = \tfrac{1}{24} \qquad P(\text{black}) = \tfrac{1}{8}$$

If the bag contains 48 marbles, how many marbles of each color are there?

12 green
8 blue
18 red
2 yellow
2 white
6 black

Glencoe Division, Macmillan/McGraw-Hill

Enrichment Worksheet 14-2

Rolling a Dodecahedron

A **dodecahedron** is a solid. It has twelve faces, and each face is a pentagon.

At the right, you see a dodecahedron whose faces are marked with the integers from 1 through 12. You can roll this dodecahedron just as you roll a number cube. With the dodecahedron, however, there are *twelve* equally likely outcomes.

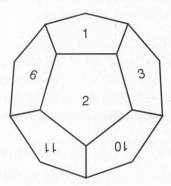

Refer to the dodecahedron shown at the right. Find the probability of each event.

1. $P(5)$

2. $P(\text{odd})$

3. $P(\text{prime})$

4. $P(\text{divisible by 5})$

5. $P(\text{less than 4})$

6. $P(\text{fraction})$

You can make your own dodecahedron by cutting out the pattern at the right. Fold along each of the solid lines. Then use tape to join the faces together so that your dodecahedron looks like the one shown above.

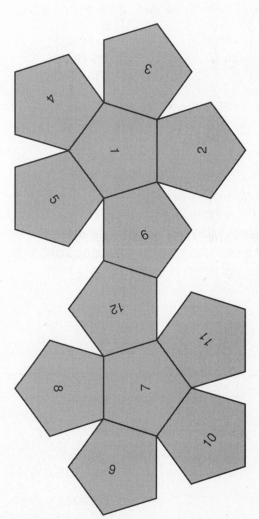

7. Roll your dodecahedron 100 times. Record your results on a separate sheet of paper, using a table like this.

Outcome	Tally	Frequency
1		
2		

8. Use your results from Exercise 7. Find the *experimental probability* for each of the events described in Exercises 1-6.

Glencoe Division, Macmillan/McGraw-Hill

Enrichment Worksheet 14-2

Rolling a Dodecahedron

A **dodecahedron** is a solid. It has twelve faces, and each face is a pentagon.

At the right, you see a dodecahedron whose faces are marked with the integers from 1 through 12. You can roll this dodecahedron just as you roll a number cube. With the dodecahedron, however, there are *twelve* equally likely outcomes.

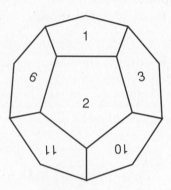

Refer to the dodecahedron shown at the right. Find the probability of each event.

1. $P(5)$ $\frac{1}{12}$ 2. $P(\text{odd})$ $\frac{1}{2}$

3. $P(\text{prime})$ $\frac{5}{12}$ 4. $P(\text{divisible by 5})$ $\frac{1}{6}$

5. $P(\text{less than 4})$ $\frac{1}{4}$ 6. $P(\text{fraction})$ **0**

You can make your own dodecahedron by cutting out the pattern at the right. Fold along each of the solid lines. Then use tape to join the faces together so that your dodecahedron looks like the one shown above.

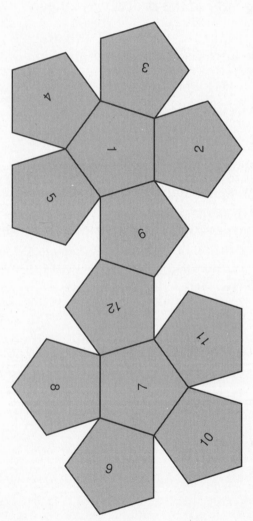

7. Roll your dodecahedron 100 times. Record your results on a separate sheet of paper, using a table like this.

Outcome	Tally	Frequency
1		
2		

Answers will vary.

8. Use your results from Exercise 7. Find the *experimental probability* for each of the events described in Exercises 1-6.   **Answers will vary.**

Glencoe Division, Macmillan/McGraw-Hill

Enrichment Worksheet 14-3

Odds

People who play games of chance often talk about **odds.** You can find the *odds in favor* of an event by using this formula.

$$\text{odds in favor} = \frac{\text{number of ways an event can occur}}{\text{number of ways the event cannot occur}}$$

With the spinner shown at the right, for example, this is how you would find the odds in favor of the event *prime number*.

There are four prime numbers (2, 3, 5, 7). $\rightarrow \frac{4}{6} = \frac{2}{3}$
Six numbers are not prime (1, 4, 6, 8, 9, 10). $\rightarrow$

The odds in favor of the event *prime number* are $\frac{2}{3}$ or 2 to 3.

Suppose that you spin the spinner shown above. Find the odds in favor of each event.

1. number greater than 3

2. number less than or equal to 6

3. even number

4. odd number

5. multiple of 3

6. factor of 10

To find the *odds against* an event, you use this formula.

$$\text{odds against} = \frac{\text{number of ways an event cannot occur}}{\text{number of ways the event can occur}}$$

Suppose that you roll a number cube with 1, 2, 3, 4, 5, and 6 marked on its faces. Find the odds against each event.

7. number less than 5

8. number greater than or equal to 2

9. even number

10. odd number

11. number divisible by 3

12. factor of 12

13. **CHALLENGE** The probability of an event is $\frac{2}{3}$. What are the odds in favor of the event? the odds against the event?

Enrichment Worksheet 14-3

Odds

People who play games of chance often talk about **odds.** You can find the *odds in favor* of an event by using this formula.

$$\text{odds in favor} = \frac{\text{number of ways an event can occur}}{\text{number of ways the event cannot occur}}$$

With the spinner shown at the right, for example, this is how you would find the odds in favor of the event *prime number*.

There are four prime numbers (2, 3, 5, 7). → $\frac{4}{6} = \frac{2}{3}$
Six numbers are not prime (1, 4, 6, 8, 9, 10). →

The odds in favor of the event *prime number* are $\frac{2}{3}$ or 2 to 3.

Suppose that you spin the spinner shown above. Find the odds in favor of each event.

1. number greater than 3   **7 to 3**

2. number less than or equal to 6
   3 to 2

3. even number   **1 to 1**

4. odd number   **1 to 1**

5. multiple of 3   **3 to 7**

6. factor of 10   **2 to 3**

To find the *odds against* an event, you use this formula.

$$\text{odds against} = \frac{\text{number of ways an event cannot occur}}{\text{number of ways the event can occur}}$$

Suppose that you roll a number cube with 1, 2, 3, 4, 5, and 6 marked on its faces. Find the odds against each event.

7. number less than 5   **1 to 2**

8. number greater than or equal to 2
   1 to 5

9. even number   **1 to 1**

10. odd number   **1 to 1**

11. number divisible by 3   **2 to 1**

12. factor of 12   **1 to 5**

13. **CHALLENGE** The probability of an event is $\frac{2}{3}$. What are the odds in favor of the event? the odds against the event?
    2 to 1; 1 to 2

Enrichment Worksheet 14-4

Spinners and More Spinners

When you spin a spinner, it is not necessarily true that all outcomes are equally likely. With the spinner shown at the right, for example, you can see it is most likely that the pointer will stop in region A. To find probabilities on a spinner like this, you need to consider what fraction of a complete turn of the pointer is associated with each region. In the spinner at the right, region A involves about $\frac{1}{2}$ of a complete turn, so $P(A)$ is about $\frac{1}{2}$. Using the same reasoning, $P(B)$ is about $\frac{1}{4}$, $P(C)$ is about $\frac{1}{8}$, and $P(D)$ is about $\frac{1}{8}$.

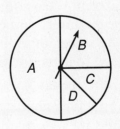

Estimate each probability.

1.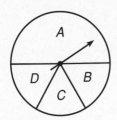

$P(A)$:

$P(B)$:

$P(C)$:

$P(D)$:

2.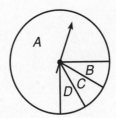

$P(A)$:

$P(B)$:

$P(C)$:

$P(D)$:

3.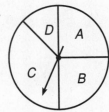

$P(A)$:

$P(B)$:

$P(C)$:

$P(D)$:

Sketch a spinner that satisfies the given conditions.

4. $P(A) = \frac{1}{2}$

$P(B) = \frac{1}{2}$

$P(C) = \frac{1}{12}$

$P(D) = \frac{1}{12}$

5. $P(A) = \frac{1}{4}$

$P(B) = \frac{1}{4}$

$P(C) = \frac{1}{3}$

$P(D) = \frac{1}{6}$

6. $P(A) = \frac{1}{8}$

$P(B) = \frac{5}{8}$

$P(C) = \frac{3}{16}$

$P(D) = \frac{1}{16}$

7. CHALLENGE Use the spinner at the right. Estimate each probability.

$P(A)$:

$P(B)$:

$P(C)$:

$P(D)$:

115

Enrichment Worksheet 14-4

Spinners and More Spinners

When you spin a spinner, it is not necessarily true that all outcomes are equally likely. With the spinner shown at the right, for example, you can see it is most likely that the pointer will stop in region A. To find probabilities on a spinner like this, you need to consider what fraction of a complete turn of the pointer is associated with each region. In the spinner at the right, region

A involves about $\frac{1}{2}$ of a complete turn, so $P(A)$ is about $\frac{1}{2}$. Using

the same reasoning, $P(B)$ is about $\frac{1}{4}$, $P(C)$ is about $\frac{1}{8}$, and $P(D)$

is about $\frac{1}{8}$.

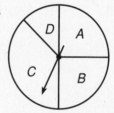

Estimate each probability.

1.

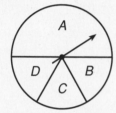

$P(A)$: about $\frac{1}{2}$

$P(B)$: about $\frac{1}{6}$

$P(C)$: about $\frac{1}{6}$

$P(D)$: about $\frac{1}{6}$

2.

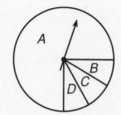

$P(A)$: about $\frac{3}{4}$

$P(B)$: about $\frac{1}{12}$

$P(C)$: about $\frac{1}{12}$

$P(D)$: about $\frac{1}{12}$

3.

$P(A)$: about $\frac{1}{4}$

$P(B)$: about $\frac{1}{4}$

$P(C)$: about $\frac{3}{8}$

$P(D)$: about $\frac{1}{8}$

Sketch a spinner that satisfies the given conditions. Sketches may vary.

4. $P(A) = \frac{1}{2}$

$P(B) = \frac{1}{2}$

$P(C) = \frac{1}{12}$

$P(D) = \frac{1}{12}$

5. $P(A) = \frac{1}{4}$

$P(B) = \frac{1}{4}$

$P(C) = \frac{1}{3}$

$P(D) = \frac{1}{6}$

6. $P(A) = \frac{1}{8}$

$P(B) = \frac{5}{8}$

$P(C) = \frac{3}{16}$

$P(D) = \frac{1}{16}$

7. CHALLENGE   Use the spinner at the right. Estimate each probability.

$P(A)$: about $\frac{1}{4}$ $P(B)$: about $\frac{1}{4}$

$P(C)$: about $\frac{1}{4}$ $P(D)$: about $\frac{1}{4}$

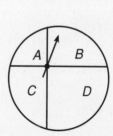

Enrichment Worksheet 14-5

Listing Outcomes in a Table

Suppose that you spin the two spinners below. What is the probability that the sum of the numbers you spin is 5?

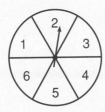

First Spinner

	1	2	3	4
1	2	3	4	5
2	3	4	5	6
3	4	5	6	7
4	5	6	7	8
5	6	7	8	9
6	7	8	9	10

Second Spinner

To find this probability, you first need to count the outcomes. One way to do this is to use a table of sums like the one at the right. From the table, it is easy to see that there are 24 outcomes. It is also easy to see that, in 4 of these outcomes, the sum of the numbers is 5. So, the probability that the sum of the numbers is 5 is $\frac{4}{24}$, or $\frac{1}{6}$.

Use the spinners and the table above. Find each probability.

1. P(sum is 8)

2. P(sum is 12)

3. P(sum is greater than 6)

4. P(sum is less than or equal to 10)

Suppose you roll two number cubes. Each cube is marked with 1, 2, 3, 4, 5, and 6 on its faces. Find each probability. (Hint: On a separate sheet of paper, make a chart like the one above.)

5. P(sum is 9)

6. P(sum is 3)

7. P(sum is an even number)

8. P(sum is a multiple of 3)

9. P(sum is a prime number)

10. P(sum is a factor of 12)

11. P(sum is greater than 12)

12. P(sum is less than 6)

13. *CHALLENGE* Here is a set of probabilities associated with two spinners.

P(sum is 4) = $\frac{1}{6}$ P(sum is 6) = $\frac{1}{3}$

P(sum is 8) = $\frac{1}{3}$ P(sum is 10) = $\frac{1}{6}$

In the space at the right, sketch the two spinners.

Glencoe Division, Macmillan/McGraw-Hill

Enrichment Worksheet 14-5

Listing Outcomes in a Table

Suppose that you spin the two spinners below. What is the probability that the sum of the numbers you spin is 5?

To find this probability, you first need to count the outcomes. One way to do this is to use a table of sums like the one at the right. From the table, it is easy to see that there are 24 outcomes. It is also easy to see that, in 4 of these outcomes, the sum of the numbers is 5. So, the probability that the sum of the numbers is 5 is $\frac{4}{24}$, or $\frac{1}{6}$.

First Spinner

Second Spinner		1	2	3	4
	1	2	3	4	5
	2	3	4	5	6
	3	4	5	6	7
	4	5	6	7	8
	5	6	7	8	9
	6	7	8	9	10

Use the spinners and the table above. Find each probability.

1. P(sum is 8) $\frac{1}{8}$

2. P(sum is 12) **0**

3. P(sum is greater than 6) $\frac{5}{12}$

4. P(sum is less than or equal to 10) **1**

Suppose you roll two number cubes. Each cube is marked with 1, 2, 3, 4, 5, and 6 on its faces. Find each probability. (<u>Hint</u>: On a separate sheet of paper, make a chart like the one above.)

5. P(sum is 9) $\frac{1}{9}$

6. P(sum is 3) $\frac{1}{18}$

7. P(sum is an even number) $\frac{1}{2}$

8. P(sum is a multiple of 3) $\frac{1}{3}$

9. P(sum is a prime number) $\frac{15}{36}$

10. P(sum is a factor of 12) $\frac{1}{3}$

11. P(sum is greater than 12) **0**

12. P(sum is less than 6) $\frac{5}{18}$

13. CHALLENGE Here is a set of probabilities associated with two spinners. **Answers may vary.**

P(sum is 4) $= \frac{1}{6}$ P(sum is 6) $= \frac{1}{3}$

P(sum is 8) $= \frac{1}{3}$ P(sum is 10) $= \frac{1}{6}$

In the space at the right, sketch the two spinners.

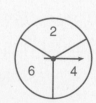

Enrichment Worksheet 14-6

Dependent Events

If the result of one event affects the result of a second event, the events are called **dependent**. For example, suppose you draw one card from the set of cards shown at the right, but do not replace it. Then you draw a second card. What is the probability that you will draw the T, then an L?

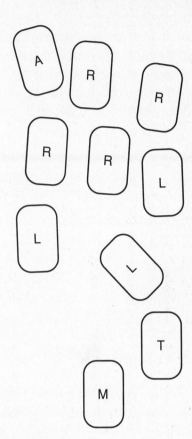

First find the probability of drawing the T.

$P(\text{T}) = \frac{1}{10}$ ← There is 1 card marked T.
         ← There are 10 cards in all.

Then find the probability of drawing an L after drawing the T.

$P(\text{L after T}) = \frac{3}{9}$ ← There are 3 cards marked L.
              ← There are 9 cards left.

Now multiply.

$P(\text{T, then L}) = P(\text{T}) \times P(\text{L after T})$

$= \frac{1}{10} \times \frac{3}{9}$

$= \frac{3}{90} \text{ or } \frac{1}{30}$

The probability of drawing the T, then an L, is $\frac{1}{30}$.

A card is drawn from the set of cards above, and it is not replaced. Then a second card is drawn. Find each probability.

1. $P(\text{A, then M})$

2. $P(\text{T, then R})$

3. $P(\text{L, then R})$

4. $P(\text{R, then L})$

5. $P(\text{L, then L})$

6. $P(\text{M, then M})$

A bag contains two red marbles and four blue marbles. Three marbles are pulled from the bag, one at a time, and they are not replaced. Find each probability.

7. $P(\text{blue, then red, then blue})$

8. $P(\text{red, then blue, then red})$

9. $P(\text{three blue marbles})$

10. $P(\text{three red marbles})$

11. CHALLENGE Refer to the cards at the top of the page. Suppose that you draw two cards at once. What do you think is the probability that you draw an R and an L?

Enrichment Worksheet 14-6

Dependent Events

If the result of one event affects the result of a second event, the events are called **dependent**. For example, suppose you draw one card from the set of cards shown at the right, but do not replace it. Then you draw a second card. What is the probability that you will draw the T, then an L?

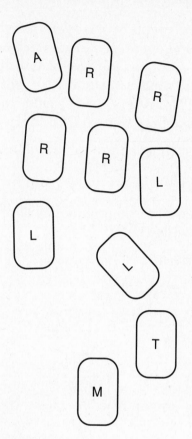

First find the probability of drawing the T.

$$P(T) = \tfrac{1}{10} \quad \begin{array}{l} \leftarrow \text{ There is 1 card marked T.} \\ \leftarrow \text{ There are 10 cards in all.} \end{array}$$

Then find the probability of drawing an L after drawing the T.

$$P(L \text{ after } T) = \tfrac{3}{9} \quad \begin{array}{l} \leftarrow \text{ There are 3 cards marked L.} \\ \leftarrow \text{ There are 9 cards left.} \end{array}$$

Now multiply.

$$P(T, \text{ then } L) = P(T) \times P(L \text{ after } T)$$

$$= \tfrac{1}{10} \times \tfrac{3}{9}$$

$$= \tfrac{3}{90} \text{ or } \tfrac{1}{30}$$

The probability of drawing the T, then an L, is $\tfrac{1}{30}$.

A card is drawn from the set of cards above, and it is not replaced. Then a second card is drawn. Find each probability.

1. $P(A, \text{ then } M)$ $\tfrac{1}{90}$

2. $P(T, \text{ then } R)$ $\tfrac{2}{45}$

3. $P(L, \text{ then } R)$ $\tfrac{2}{15}$

4. $P(R, \text{ then } L)$ $\tfrac{2}{15}$

5. $P(L, \text{ then } L)$ $\tfrac{1}{15}$

6. $P(M, \text{ then } M)$ 0

A bag contains two red marbles and four blue marbles. Three marbles are pulled from the bag, one at a time, and they are not replaced. Find each probability.

7. $P(\text{blue, then red, then blue})$ $\tfrac{1}{5}$

8. $P(\text{red, then blue, then red})$ $\tfrac{1}{15}$

9. $P(\text{three blue marbles})$ $\tfrac{1}{5}$

10. $P(\text{three red marbles})$ 0

11. **CHALLENGE** Refer to the cards at the top of the page. Suppose that you draw two cards at once. What do you think is the probability that you draw an R and an L?

$\tfrac{4}{15}$ **(It is equal to $P(L, \text{ then } R) + P(R, \text{ then } L)$.)**

Glencoe Division, Macmillan/McGraw-Hill